The
Cichlids
Yearbook

Volume 6

*Ad Konings (Editor),
Mary Bailey and
Martin Geerts (Co-Editors)*

CICHLID PRESS

1	
2	3	4

Cover photographs:
1 - *Haplochromis* "blue scraper"; bicolor male from Makobe Island, Lake Victoria, Tanzania. Photo by Ole Seehausen.
2 - *Aulonocara baenschi;* male at Nkhomo Reef, Lake Malaŵi.
3 - *Crenicichla regani;* male from the Rio Arapiuns, Brazil. Photo by Frank Warzel.
4 - *Tropheus cf. brichardi;* male from Msalaba, Lake Tanganyika, Tanzania.

Mary Bailey (Crediton, UK) corrected the manuscripts and translated the German and French articles.

The editor wishes to thank the following persons who supplied various cichlids for photographic purposes:
Peter Baasch (Stegen, Germany)
Marc Danhieux (Mal-Ta-Vi, Hohenahr-Erda, Germany)
Laif DeMason (Old World Exotic Fish, Homestead, Florida, USA)
Stuart Grant (Lake Malawi Cichlid Centre, Salima, Malawi)
Toby Veall (Rift Valley Tropicals, Lusaka, Zambia)

ISBN 3-928457-34-9

Cichlid Press, Ahornweg 3, D-31864 Lauenau.

Contents

Tanganyika Cichlids

Malawi Cichlids

Other African Cichlids

Central American Cichlids

South American Cichlids

Cichlid Literatim

Petenia splendida. Photo by Don Danko.

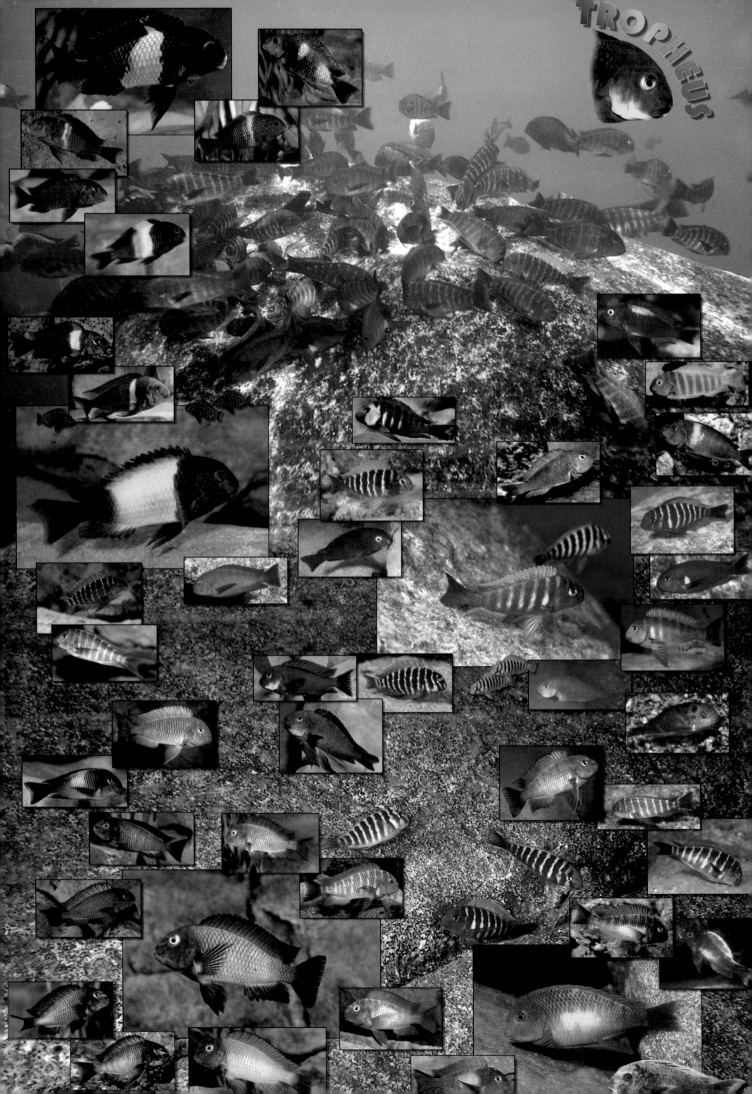

TROPHEUS

Introduction

On April 1st, 1996, Saulos Mwale, head diver and manager of Stuart Grant's fish collecting station in Malaŵi, died after a few weeks of hospitalisation. I had known him for more than 15 years, and I will greatly miss him and his knowledge of the lake and extraordinary skill at collecting cichlids.

During the past 5 years Madagascar and its endemic cichlid fauna have been the focus of much attention. Although it transpires that many habitats have been destroyed by human activity, several new cichlid species, together with others already known, have been located and brought back alive for aquarists to enjoy. Two new yearbook contributors, Dr. Patrick de Rham and Jean-Claude Nourissat, are the explorers most involved in obtaining such specimens, and they share their knowledge of Madagascar cichlids with us in this volume (Madagascar cichlids are also the subject matter in Martin Geerts' contribution discussing the age of cichlids).

Jean-Claude Nourissat (Toulon, France) ranks foremost among the world's cichlid-collectors and has discovered numerous new species in Central and South America as well as in Madagascar. He has been president of the French Cichlid Association for a very long time and has for many years devoted all of his free time to cichlids and cichlid collecting. His contribution tells us about the rediscovery of two Madagascan cichlids.

Dr. Patrick de Rham (Lausanne, Switzerland), a biologist by both profession and inclination, has travelled to all the corners of the globe, gaining a wealth of experience and information on cichlid biotopes. He has visited Madagascar 7 times, and during his most recent expedition was able to collect a few specimens of *Oxylapia polli*, a species restricted to fast-flowing water and with a very limited distribution.

Other authors who are contributing for the first time are here briefly introduced in the order in which their articles appear:

Volker Puttberg (Dinslaken, Germany) is an experienced Tanganyika specialist who has kept and bred almost all the species known from the lake. Besides breeding some *Cyprichromis* species, he has also been able to capture the beautiful coloration of these fishes on film.

Benthochromis tricoti is a very popular cichlid, but only a handful of aquarists have been able to breed it in captivity. They include Paolo Salvagiani (Forli, Italy), one of the founders of the Italian Cichlid Association, who has studied biology and shares his knowledge as coeditor of their bimonthly magazine.

Dr. Jay Stauffer Jr. (Pennsylvania State University, USA) needs no introduction as he is one of the leading scientists working on Malaŵi cichlids. He has published a number of descriptions of cichlid species and many more are planned. His Ph.D. student Karen Kellogg is studying the importance of colour in mate choice in several mbuna species, and together they report on their findings and on the types of field and laboratory studies they are conducting.

Rusty Wessel (Louisville, USA) is a committee chairman of the American Cichlid Association and a lifelong aficionado of Central American cichlids. His article describes the discovery of a new cichlid species in Honduras, which has recently been named after him: *Theraps wesseli*.

Anybody who has kept Malaŵi cichlids will have heard of Stuart Grant (Salima, Malaŵi), who has been exporting Malaŵi cichlids all over the world since 1972, but is best known for his uncompromising hospitality to anybody interested in observing Malaŵi cichlids in their natural biotope. His contribution describes the current situation regarding cichlid collecting in East Africa.

Finally, I would like to thank the following friends for their support and hospitality: Laif DeMason (Homestead, Florida), Gary Kratochvil (San Antonio, Texas), Juan Miguel Artigas (San Luis Potosí, Mexico), Toby Veall (Mpulungu, Zambia), Jeanne and Chris Blignaut (Mpulungu, Zambia), and last, but not least, Stuart Grant.

Ad Konings

LAKE TANGANYIKA CICHLIDS

Bathybates: beautiful predators from the depths

Ad Konings

The cichlids of Lake Tanganyika form the most variable species flock found in any of African lakes, although the total number of recognised species is smaller than that of either Lake Malaŵi or Lake Victoria. The huge diversity in morphology and breeding behaviour found among Tanganyikan cichlids probably stems from the fact that the flock originated from several different lineages. Almost all of the species that can be collected alive are being kept by aquarists all over the world, and there are in fact very few such species which have never been bred in captivity. Almost all of the species currently kept are collected in the upper 30 metres of the water column, most of them in rocky habitats. There is, however, a large group of species, including those of the genus *Bathybates*, which live at much deeper levels. We know about them only from fishermen, who catch such species on hook and line, usually baited with pieces of fish (and from experimental trawls and gill net collections). Cichlids have a closed swim bladder and thus cannot adjust their buoyancy instantaneously by releasing some of the gases in the bladder. In cichlids the process takes time, and when a

cichlid is caught at a depth of 100 metres and immediately hauled to the surface, it does not have enough time to adjust the gas content of its swim bladder to the much lower pressure at the surface. As a result the bladder swells and squashes the other internal organs, and often parts of the gut are forced out of the body cavity, via either the anal pore or the mouth. This process is irreversible and the fish dies within a few minutes if not already dead before it is hauled into the boat.

It has been known for a long time that the species belonging to the genus *Bathybates* have very characteristically coloured males which are very attractive. Initially there was hardly any interest in this group of species because all of them were too big, attaining a length of 30 to 40 cm. During the last decade the number of cichlid hobbyists keeping large fishes in large tanks has increased dramatically, and now there are in fact many aquarists interested in keeping large Tanganyika cichlids. Of course, *Bathybates* species rank high on their "want" lists, but apart from a few single specimens, usually *Bathybates minor*, these predators remain in their natural habitat unless being eaten by the locals or Europeans — *Bathybates* species have an excellent taste.

In order to accommodate the requests of the importers in the western world,

1. *Bathybates minor* is the only member of its genus which is exported as an aquarium fish on a fairly regular basis.
Facing page, from top to bottom: *Bathybates fasciatus*, *B. ferox*, *B. horni*, *B. leo*, *B. vittatus*, and *B. minor* (with prey still in its mouth).

1. *Bathybates graueri* has recently been exported for the aquarium trade.
2. *Limnothrissa miodon*, the largest of the two species of herring found in the lake.

exporters around the lake have tried to collect *Bathybates* alive. Very little is known of the biology of these fishes and it has therefore been almost impossible to find an area where such species can be caught in shallow water, although some species are regularly seen in the catches of the Capenta or Ndaga fishermen, who fish primarily for the small lake sardines in surface waters. There is thus a chance of obtaining a number of live *Bathybates* by screening the freshly-caught sardines, and the promise of reward is enough to motivate the fishermen to keep the occasional *Bathybates* alive. Even so, very few specimens have been exported to date and almost all of these were *B. minor* and juvenile *B. fasciatus,* the two species apparently most often seen among the schools of sardines in surface waters; both species are also regularly found at depths of between 120 and 200 metres (Coulter, 1991).

B. minor, as its name indicates, is the smallest *Bathybates* species and lives among the large shoals of lake sardines, *Stolothrissa tanganicae* and *Limnothrissa miodon.* It does not behave as a pursuit hunter, but instead makes surprise attacks on prey fishes. Its coloration and size are similar to those of its prey, and it may be that the sardines mistake the voracious predator for one of their own kind. One of the accompanying photos shows that *B. minor,* although rather small, feeds on prey of a size similar to itself. In the aquarium its feeding behaviour remains typical. The food is targeted and seized with a lightning dart, and large chunks are swallowed whole. The size of the food morsels that it can hold in its mouth is remarkable. Initially I had to feed a single specimen, kept in a tank with *B. fasciatus,* live fishes, but within two weeks it was devouring large chunks of shrimp mix (consisting of shrimps, peas, and spirulina) as if they were live sardines.

The maximum total length of *B. minor* is about 20 cm, but most of the specimens I have seen (around the lake and in importers' tanks) measured between 8 and 12 cm. All *Bathybates* are mouthbrooders and have very large eggs. Poll (1956) reports a 17.5 cm long female which held 60 large (approx. 6 mm) eggs! *B. minor* has spawned in the aquarium (Allen, 1996) but details of its spawning behaviour are not yet known. All the imported specimens I have seen were very likely juveniles or females as none of them exhibited the male colour pattern of four horizontal black stripes. Females are very silvery without any markings, but it is not known whether non-breeding or juvenile males exhibit the same pattern.

Bathybates fasciatus and *B. leo* are two further common species which appear to feed exclusively on sardines and are usually found together with their prey. Interestingly Poll (1956) reports that *B. fasciatus* could be caught *at night* with hook and line with sardines as bait. Juvenile *B. fasciatus* seem to mix with the sardines and are frequently collected with them in surface waters. In the aquarium they display a behaviour different from that of *B. minor. B. fasciatus* is a true pursuit hunter and needs a very large tank in which it can hunt its prey. I have been able to keep *B. fasciatus* on a diet of regular aquarium fare, even flake food (!), but the single specimen I kept met its death by getting stuck under a rock while hunting a small fish that hid under it. *B. fasciatus* normally hunts in open water where it swims swiftly after its prey; obstacles such as rocks are hardly ever found in its path. *B. leo* and adult *B. fasciatus* are usually found in deep to very deep water, and both have been caught at depths of 200 metres, just above the anoxic region of the lake. Adult specimens are normally caught on hook and line and males of both species have a very attractive pigmentation pattern. *B. fasciatus* is the only species of the seven known that I have seen under water. On three occasions two or three individuals were seen a few metres above the bottom at a depth of 35-40 metres. On another occasion I have seen a very large individual with male coloration in water as shallow as 10 metres (Kala Island, June 1994). On all these occasions I was able to catch only a glimpse of the fishes as they maintained a large flight distance.

The maximum recorded size of *B. fasciatus* is 41 cm and that of *B. leo* 35.5 cm (Coulter, 1991). An adult male would, of course, be a spectacular inhabitant for any large aquarium, but it has yet to be determined whether or not these pursuit hunters can adequately be kept in captivity. As in all *Bathybates*, females are silvery and exhibit a faint pattern paralleling the markings found in males. It seems that *B. leo* and adult *B. fasciatus*, together with *B. minor*, are the only species of this genus which are found in the open water column, with the first two normally found at great depths. It is thus possible that breeding in these three species may take place in open water. Juvenile *B. fasciatus* are regularly caught in shallow water over sand, perhaps indicating that females release their offspring in such habitats.

Juvenile *B. ferox* can sometimes be found in beach seine catches together with young *B. fasciatus* and *B. minor*. *B. ferox* is another large species with a recorded maximum length of 36 cm, but it is not as streamlined as the pursuit hunters *B. fasciatus* and *B. leo*. Stomach contents analysis of *B. ferox* has revealed mainly bottom-dwelling cichlids (e.g. *Xenotilapia* spp.), so it probably exploits a different food source to the sardine-hunters of the open water. Adults have also been found in shallow water, although it is not known whether they came here to hunt or to breed, or were females releasing their offspring. Poll (1956) recorded a gravid female with a swollen abdomen completely filled with 6.5 mm large eggs. The greatest depth at which *B. ferox* has been caught is 70 metres, whereas all the other species, with the possible exception of the rare *B. horni*, have been caught at depths of more than 160 metres.

B. horni seems to be a rare species (Coulter, 1991) and has rarely been caught on hook and line. I have seen some specimens which were caught in a gill net near Kipili together with *B. ferox*. *B. horni* is

streamlined like *B. leo* and *B. fasciatus* and may thus be a pursuit hunter, albeit in a different area or habitat. *B. horni* can attain a total length of more than 30 cm.

B. graueri also attains a maximum length of about 30 cm and adult specimens are sometimes caught in shallow water. Recently the first live specimens (three adults: two males and one female) were imported into Germany, and it seems likely that this species can be maintained in an aquarium as long as adequate room for swimming is provided. I was unable to change this predator's diet from live cichlids to regular aquarium fare during the three weeks I kept a single specimen. As soon as my small stock of shell-dwelling *Neolamprologus brevis* (rejected stock with gill defects) was reduced to a few specimens I took the fish back to the wholesaler (Maltavi) who had kindly lent me the specimen. *B. graueri* is normally found near the bottom where it preys on sand-dwelling cichlids such as *Xenotilapia* spp. (Coulter, 1991). In the aquarium, however, it behaves rather like an open water species, rarely swimming close to the bottom. It is thus likely that *B. graueri* cruises at a certain distance from the bottom while searching for prey.

The seventh species, *B. vittatus*, also preys on cichlids rather than sardines. Some individuals have been taken at depths of more than 200 metres and others in shallow areas over a muddy bottom. The maximum recorded length for *B. vittatus* is 42 cm, which is thus the largest member of the genus. *B. vittatus* has a remarkable scale pattern in which "normal"-sized scales are embedded among numerous tiny scales. The function of this type of squamation, as of many other features of *Bathybates*, is not known.

It is likely that the breeding behaviour of *Bathybates* species can be determined only by dedicated aquarists, as probably all species breed at a deep level, too deep for direct observation by divers using SCUBA gear. Because these fascinating cichlids are too difficult to collect in significant numbers in the wild, I hope that in the not too distant future it will be possible to obtain captive-raised *Bathybates*.

References

ALLEN, B. (1996) Spawning *Bathybates minor*—an aquarium first. *Cichlid News* 5(2); pp 22-24.

COULTER, G.W. (1991) *Lake Tanganyika and its life*. Oxford University Press, London & New York.

POLL, M. (1956) *Exploration hydrobiologique du lac Tanganika (1946-1947) Résultats scientifiques. Poissons cichlidae*. Vol. III, fasc. 5B. Inst. royal Sci nat. Belg., Tervuren, Belgium.

CYPRICHROMIS

Volker Puttberg

Cyprichromis sp. "leptosoma jumbo", from Kitumba, Zaïre, is among the most popular Tanganyika cichlids kept by aquarists. Besides an all-blue and an all-yellow morph there are many morphs exhibiting an intermediate pattern. The smaller photos on the left and above show the change in colour pattern in the same fish during an 18 month period (the third image (left photo) shows the male from the other side). The presence of yellow pigment in a young male is a good indication that such an individual will become completely yellow in adulthood. The "Kitumba Leptosoma" is a very variable variant and exhibits the most intense colour of all known *Cyprichromis*. All photos by Volker Puttberg.

richromis pavo from Zaïre. Males do not seem to exhibit polychromatism, at
ot in Zaïrean populations.

This *Cyprichromis* species, imported under the trade name of "Cyprichromis
(by MalTaVi, Germany) is possibly a geographical variant of *C. pavo*. In
st to other members of this genus, in which males differ most prominently in
our of the tail, males of *C. cf. pavo* differ mainly in the colour of the anal fin.
acteristic and beautiful feature of this variant is the elongate ventral fins. Its
our is reminiscent of that of *C. pavo*: the male constructs a small spawning-
digging with his mouth and fanning with his fins. Females are led to the pit
eck" at the male's ventral fins after picking up the eggs. Less dominant males
so defend territories along the sides of the tank or on slates leaning against
ss. Photos by Volker Puttberg.

3

1. *Cyprichromis microlepidotus* "kassei" from Zaïre. The dark markings in the yellow tail seem to be characteristic of this variant.
2 and 3. *Cyprichromis microlepidotus*. This very attractively coloured male was sent with a shipment of *C. microlepidotus* from Bemba, Zaïre, but may not come from this area.

Problems with breeding *Benthochromis tricoti*

Paolo Salvagiani

Readers of the Cichlids Yearbook will undoubtedly remember the interesting article by René Krüter on the beautiful Tanganyika cichlid *Benthochromis tricoti*, published in volume 1. I shall therefore refrain from going over aspects that have already been dealt with. What I intend to do, however, is to concentrate on my personal experience with aquarium reproduction of this fish. To be honest, this experience is somewhat limited and incomplete, and thus, rather than shedding light on the subject, raises new questions. Unfortunately the death of the only female which regularly completed the mouthbrooding period has made further investigation impossible. Publication of the relevant data may thus seem premature, yet I believe it to be more than useful because very little, as far as I am aware, has been published on the subject, despite the fact that this fish has been regularly imported for several years and has also been bred in captivity.

I gained my experience with five individuals —two males and three females— reared in a 650 litre tank. The water was as follows: pH 8.5, GH 12, KH 9, electrical conductivity 400 µS, nitrite-free, nitrates <20mg/litre. Ten individuals of *Cyathopharynx furcifer* (Burundi) and a pair of *Altolamprologus calvus* (Zaïre) shared the tank with the five *tricoti* without any apparent incompatibility. The tank ends each contained large rock masses over 30 cm high, each topped by a large flat rock with a diameter of about 35 cm. Food consisted of adult *Artemia salina* (brine shrimp) plus dry food (flake and pellets).

I obtained a pair of *B. tricoti* in November 1993 and the other three specimens from a different source some months later. It is worth mentioning that the two males can be identified by small differences in morphology and coloration: one is a little slimmer with slightly wider longitudinal sky-blue streaks and has darker gill covers. I believe it likely that this small difference can be attributed to geographical variation. I further believe that crossbreeding individuals from different origins should be avoided.

At the beginning of Spring 1994 the two males —by then fully developed— started courting and commenced fin displays, and this led to a peculiar light-oriented territoriality. One male dominated when the three fluorescent tubes were off (until 1 pm) and the other would take control when the lights were on (until 10 pm)! Courtship became steadily more intense until one evening I observed mating for the first time. A female followed the dominant male onto one of the large flat rocks, chosen by the male as his territory, and

The female *Benthochromis tricoti* picks up an egg she has just laid. The male waits in the background. Photo by Paolo Salvagiani.

started to clean it. She used her mouth to brush away sand grains as the male had done during his courtship.

Soon afterwards the female started a slow, quivering swimming pattern, moving in a straight line for about 10 cm while keeping her abdomen in close contact with the stone. The small ovipositor, which had appeared some hours earlier, was dragging over the stone. The female then backed up, swimming backwards, and raised the rear part of her body while keeping her mouth against the substrate. After a few dry runs the female started to deposit eggs and collect them in her mouth. All the ivory-coloured eggs (6 in total, with a diameter of about 2 mm) were laid in about 15 minutes. While the female was laying eggs the male circled imposingly above her with his fins erect and mouth wide open, descending every now and then to lie across the female's path. When his genital region came close to the female's mouth he would give an intense quiver while emitting seminal fluid, which was just visible as a milky cloud. The female quickly drew this into her mouth by opening and closing her gill covers repeatedly. The entire spawning "ceremony" lasted for approximately half an hour after which the female withdrew into a corner of the tank, joining the other *tricoti*.

Spawning had occurred, but this did not necessarily mean that the reproductive process would be completed. I was aware that the *B. tricoti* owned by two other members of the AIC (Associazione Italiana Ciclidofili) had mated

regularly but without the successful completion of the mouthbrooding period. As far as the mating pattern is concerned, it is interesting to note how this differs from tank to tank. My friend

Claudio Barberis had always observed mating taking place on the sand which the pair had accumulated in a corner of the tank. The female would collect the eggs from the bottom by moving her pectoral fins energetically, thus stirring up the eggs. And, curiously, spawning in Enzo Marino's aquarium always takes place along the dark sides of the tank (i.e. vertically) despite the presence of horizontally-placed flat slabs.

Ad Konings recently observed a breeding colony of *B. tricoti* at a depth of 28 metres at Cape Mpimbwe (Msalaba, Tanzania), where the males had constructed large sand cones onto which they attempted to attract females. Previous observations in Zambia had indicated that mating in this species occurred on the steep rock walls which drop towards the bottom at a depth of more than 30 metres.

Returning to my own experiences, the following observations were made: the morning after spawning I noticed that the female, during feeding time, picked up a flake and (as usually happens with these fishes) a bubble of air from the surface. When she expelled the air two eggs were drawn out of her oral cavity. So, despite the lack of any visible bulging of the mouth cavity, the eggs still seemed to be there. I stopped feeding for the next few days and the continuous "chewing" movements, typical of oral incubators, displayed by the female, kept my hopes high. Ten days after spawning I could no longer resist the temptation and offered dry fish food again and, as before, the air bubble expelled by the *B. tricoti* female was accompanied by something else. This time it was a larva which I hurriedly netted, whereupon I found myself confronted with an unusual little creature just 6 mm long, which at first looked like some kind of deep-sea fish

Left: the female "inhales" sperm released by the male in order to fertilize the eggs inside her mouth.
Facing page: A displaying male *Bentho-chromis tricoti*.
Photos by Paolo Salvagiani.

in miniature. It had an enormous mouth with a protruding lower jaw, while the body and tail were by contrast very small. The fins were virtually nonexistent and, most surprisingly, the yolk sac had completely disappeared; thus in just ten days at about 25° C its food reserves had been completely exhausted.

In order to rescue the other fry I had to catch the female, a somewhat laborious task which I finally achieved successfully. By carefully opening her mouth, while still in the water, I was able to coax her into expelling the other fry. In terms of numbers the result was meagre: just three, but they were in good health. The *Benthochromis* had reproduced! I placed the four fry in a floating cage fitted with a finely meshed screen so that water was able to circulate freely. I immediately gave them *Artemia* nauplii which seemed almost too small for those large mouths. These were immediately eaten by the fry which, lacking proper buoyancy, moved erratically on their sides along the bottom of the cage, sometimes engaging in meaningless spiralling.

Over the next few days three fry died owing to causes which I am unable to explain, although I did get the impression that they had digested the *Artemia*

with some difficulty. I had noticed that after feeding the distended abdomen emptied extremely slowly, and that respiration became difficult. The fourth fry, having survived the first few days, grew amazingly quickly, and 20 days after spawning it was similar in shape to its mother, swimming normally, and able to feed on small (3-4 mm long) mosquito larvae. One month after spawning it had a length of 3 cm and at an age of three months it measured 5.5 cm.

In the meantime, at the end of June, the same female spawned again (the temperature had increased to 27° C). On the tenth day of incubation I again caught the female, which this time released five slightly longer (about 8 mm) and better developed larvae which could swim, albeit with difficulty. This time too the majority of the fry died over the first few days, but the two survivors went on to develop rapidly. Shortly afterwards the mother of these fry died, owing to an equipment failure. The other *B. tricoti* continued to mate regularly, but neither of the females successfully completed the incubation period.

These observations, while preliminary, raise the following questions:

1. How can larvae, 6-8 mm long, deprived of a yolk sac 10 days after spawning, and unable to swim freely, develop in a species which has virtually no contact with the substrate? Are they perhaps able to feed when still inside the female's mouth, given the fact that females carrying 3-4 cm long fry have been caught?

2. What is the point of having such a large mouth if *Artemia* nauplii are digested with such difficulty? In other words what do fry eat during the first few days following exhaustion of the yolk sac?

3. How come a cichlid with a size of 18-20 cm produces so few eggs —the record to my knowledge is 12 eggs— which are so small? We know that *Tropheus* also produce very few eggs, yet these are at least twice as big as those laid by *Benthochromis*.

4. Why does spawning in captivity occur in so many different ways?

5. Why is the "birth" of young so rare in the aquarium while spawning is so frequent?

For the moment the answers to these questions, and many other aspects of the life history of *B. tricoti*, remain a mystery. It is my hope that enthusiasts with a deep involvement with these fascinating cichlids will one day come up with the solutions.

On the differences between *Petrochromis polyodon* and *Petrochromis famula*

Hans-Joachim Herrmann

It is hardly surprising that in recent years almost all authors have confused *Petrochromis polyodon* and *P. famula* with each other, given that even easily differentiated species such as *P. orthognathus* and *P. fasciolatus* have been wrongly identified. We need only to leaf through the literature published to date: for example the Mergus Atlas, Volume 4, pages 670-671 of which purport to deal with *Petrochromis fasciolatus* — but the photograph shows a *Petrochromis* species, a comparable colour form of which was imported to Germany a few years ago as *Petrochromis* sp. "kasumbe". The true *P. fasciolatus* is the only *Petrochromis* species scientifically described thus far that has a slightly upward-directed mouth, ie the upper jaw is somewhat shorter than the lower. The fish on page 671, by contrast, has an underslung mouth and visibly shorter lower jaw.

The text and photo on pages 672-673 of the same work, purportedly dealing with *P. orthognathus*, are likewise of dubious validity. The photo shows a yellow-brown *Petrochromis*, similarly coloured to *Petrochromis* sp. "Moshi Yellow". The upper jaw of the fish in the photo is very long, and the mouth correspondingly underslung; moreover the lips cannot close completely given this arrangement of the jaws. *P. orthognathus*, meanwhile, is the only *Petrochromis* species with a terminal mouth, and which can close its lips almost completely! Its jaws are more-or-less the same length. The same applies, with some qualification, to *P. famula*.

The problem of differentiating *P. polyodon* and *P. famula* is far more difficult to resolve, as there is a third species (or subspecies) which has in the past been responsible for much of the confusion. Let us look at the facts (Yamaoka, 1983): *P. famula* is the deepest-bodied of the scientifically described *Petrochromis* species, with a body depth measuring 42% of standard length (S.L.). The relationship is rather different in *P. polyodon*, where body depth represents only 40.1% of S.L., ie the fish is less deep-bodied and/or more elongate. The corresponding data for the other described species range between 37.6% and 40.8%.

A further, very good differentiating character is mentioned by Yamaoka, namely the vertical width of the gap between the outer edges of the lips (as a percentage of S.L.) when the jaws are in the closed position. The data for the individual species are as follows: *P. orthognathus* has a value of only 0.1-0.8% (average 0.4%). *P. famula* can likewise close its mouth almost completely: Yamaoka's average for 5 specimens is just 0.6%. For *P. polyodon* the figure is 2.4%, and it is thus obvious that this species swims around with its lips parted. The teeth of this last species are far more visible, even when the mouth is closed, than are those of *P. famula*.

Now one may well ask why, given that Yamaoka published these data as long ago as 1983, subsequent authors (myself included!) have failed to take them into account? I believe that the above-mentioned third, possibly undescribed, species has played a part. As well as this brown, cigar-shaped *Petrochromis* species, exported by the hundred from the northern half of Lake Tanganyika, another, similarly-coloured but deeper-bodied species is periodically imported. This latter species is *P. famula*, while the "cigar-shaped" population is labelled *P. polyodon* in all the aquarium literature published to date (March, 1996). In the book *"Tanganyika Secrets"* (Konings

& Dieckhoff, 1992), my eye was caught by a *Petrochromis* on page 125, identified by the authors as *P. polyodon* from M'toto. If one compares the black-and-white illustrations in Yamaoka with the photograph, then it is immediately apparent that this fish must in fact be a *P. famula*. Moreover in the English edition of "Tanganyika Cichlids" (Konings, 1988) the type specimen of *P. famula* is pictured on page 43. The two fishes are identical in their body proportions, and just look at the mouth shape! There can thus be no doubt that the red-brown, brown-grey, or plain brown individuals with the almost terminal mouths, practically completely closed lips, and relatively short bodies, are *P. famula*.

Konings and myself have held discussions with a view to further clarifying the difficulties. The brown, cigar-shaped species with the light brown vertical bars, the almost terminal mouth, and the sometimes orange fins, may also turn out to be *P. famula*. The terminal mouth and similar pattern are points in favour of this identification, while against it is the shallower body depth in relation to S.L. As *P. famula* has a lake-wide distribution these variations may be of geographical origin; on the other hand the differences are sufficiently striking for there to be two species involved. Comparison of the photo on page 131 of "African Cichlids II, Cichlids from East Africa" (Staeck & Linke, 1995) with that in Konings (1988, page 43) demonstrates clearly that the two forms are distinguishable in terms of the body depth to length ratio. It should be noted that the fish on page 131 of Staeck & Linke is not *P. polyodon*!

The type locality of *P. polyodon* is near Mpulungu. The species found there, which I will herein term *P. polyodon*, can be found in suitable biotopes lake-wide. It is a large, elongate *Petrochromis* with a blue-grey, green-grey, or yellow-grey base colour. Depending on mood, 8-9 vertical bars may be exhibited. The mouth is always underslung and slightly open! In order to remove all doubt, Konings asked Dr Jos Snoeks to have photographs taken of the syntype of *P. polyodon*. When we saw these photos, it was immediately apparent to both that brownish coloration does not necessarily mean *P. polyodon*, but that instead body shape and mouth form are the decisive factors.

References

BAENSCH, H.A. & R. RIEHL (1995) *Mergus Aquarien Atlas*, Vol. 4. Mergus Verlag, Melle, Germany.

KONINGS, A. (1988) *Tanganyika Cichlids*. Verduijn Cichlids, Zevenhuizen, Netherlands.

KONINGS, A. & H. W. DIECKHOFF (1992) *Tanganyika Secrets*. Cichlid Press, St Leon-Rot, Germany.

STAECK, W. & H. LINKE (1995) *African Cichlids II, Cichlids from East Africa*. Tetra Verlag, Melle, Germany.

YAMAOKA, K. (1983) A revision of the cichlid fish genus *Petrochromis* from Lake Tanganyika, with description of a new species. *Jap. J. Ichthyol.*, 30 (2); pp 129-141.

1. *Petrochromis polyodon* in its natural habitat (Mpulungu, Zambia). Photo by Ad Konings.
2. *P. famula* from Burundi. Photo Hans-J. Herrmann.
3. *P. cf. famula* (the "cigar-shaped" form) from Kapampa, Zaire. Photo Hans-J. Herrman.
4. A syntype of *P. polyodon* from Mpulungu. Photo by Dr. Jos Snoeks.

LAKE MALAŴI CICHLIDS

Two long-nosed cichlids

Ad Konings

One of the two cichlids of the genus *Mylochromis* presented here is a well-known aquarium fish, known under trade names such as "Makanjila Longnose", "Pointed Nose", or "Makanjila Mola" and exported from the East coast of Lake Malaŵi since the mid eighties. For some time the eastern lake shore in Malaŵi was the only known locality where this attractive cichlid could be found. Recently, with the opening up of the Tanzanian and Mozambique shores of the lake, it has become apparent that this species has a much wider distribution than previously thought. The distribution of the Makanjila Longnose encompasses the entire eastern coast of Lake Malaŵi, from Ikombe in the north to Makanjila Point in the south. Even though this area is very large there is only a single geographical race known; it is also unusual for a species with such a wide distribution to be found on only one side of the lake (but see below). The populations found north of the Ruhuhu River in Tanzania consist of individuals

with thicker lips than those elsewhere. This variant is known as "Mylochromis Mchuse", named after one of the divers who used to work for LANYAFI, an export company which was based at Kyela, Tanzania, in the far north of the lake.

An addition

Recently I was able to observe and photograph a similar species along the western coast, specifically at Nkhata Bay and Lion's Cove (this place is locally known as "T'hoto"). Although it is likely that this species is closely related to — and may even be conspecific with — the Makanjila Longnose, for the time being I will call it *M.* sp. "lateristriga nkhata" as it seems to be geographically isolated from the well-known Longnose. The Lateristriga Nkhata has not yet been found along the northwestern coast, north of Usisya, nor along the western central or southern shores.

1. *Mylochromis* sp. "lateristriga makanjila", male at Gome, Malaŵi.
2. *M.* sp. "lateristriga makanjila" ("Mchuse"), male at Lupingu, Tanzania.
3. *M.* sp. "lateristriga makanjila", male at Chiwindi, Mozambique.
4. *M.* sp. "lateristriga nkhata", male at Nkhata Bay, Malaŵi.

This is probably the species which Jackson (1961) confused with *M. guentheri*, a sand-dwelling cichlid found in shallow water (Eccles & Trewavas, 1989). Both the Lateristriga Nkhata and the Makanjila Longnose are found in association with rocks, normally in the intermediate habitat. The Lateristriga Nkhata shares an uncommon feature with *M. guentheri*, namely that the lower jaw is shorter than the upper. There are, however, a number of characteristics which clearly distinguish the Lateristriga Nkhata from *M. guentheri*, such as a longer head, larger eye, longer lower jaw, and narrower interorbital width.

It would not surprise me if, after proper examination of specimens from the eastern as well as the western shores of the lake, both of these long-snouted forms are found to be one and the same species. At some time in the past they probably formed a single continuous population, when the lake level was much lower and the lake much smaller than at present. The rising water level subsequently separated the population into two geographically isolated sister populations, one of which remained in more or less the same position on the western coast while the eastern population was able to disperse along most of the eastern shore. The Ruhuhu River may have been a significant obstacle in its northern dispersal, and there is thus very little exchange of genetic material between the populations on either side of the river mouth.

The line

The diagonal line, characteristic of species of the genus *Mylochromis*, is blotchy in many individuals of the Makanjila Longnose. There is an interesting variability in the appearance of this diagonal line: some specimens have a continuous diagonal line running from the nape to the caudal peduncle while in other individuals it starts at the third vertical bar; in some individuals

there is a distinct gap in the diagonal line. The vertical bars, meanwhile, are barely visible. In the aquarium this variation seems to be related to the mood of the fish and under natural circumstances too, individuals with and without complete diagonal lines can be seen at the same locality. It seems likely, however, that in some populations — such as the ones found north of the Ruhuhu River in Tanzania — there is no variation and that the diagonal line is complete in all individuals of that particular population.

1. *Mylochromis* sp. "lateristriga makanjila", female at Gome, Malaŵi.
2. *M.* sp. "lateristriga nkhata", female at Nkhata Bay, Malaŵi.

Distinction

The diagonal line also provides the distinction between this species and the very similar but larger *M. lateristriga*. The diagonal line in *M. lateristriga* is solid and well defined, whereas in the Makanjila Longnose it is often irregular or incomplete. A further characteristic that distinguishes these two species is the barring pattern found on the upper body between the stripe and the dorsal fin of the Makanjila Longnose. The maximum length of both the Makanjila Longnose and the Lateristriga Nkhata is approximately 16 cm for males and about 11 cm for females. *M. lateristriga,* which is better known in the hobby as the "Giant Flame Oxyrhynchus", can attain a length of about 22 cm. All three dig in the substrate in search of invertebrates, but the prey taken by *M. lateristriga* is probably harder than that eaten by the other two. Such differences in diet are suggested by the structure of the pharyngeal teeth, which are heavy in *M. lateristriga* and small and pointed in the other two forms. Besides other morphological differences between the large *M. lateristriga* and the other two longnoses — ie a much longer snout and a smaller eye — there is also a difference in habitat preference. The characteristic habitat preferred by *M.* sp. "lateristriga makanjila" and *M.* sp. "lateristriga nkhata" consists of small rocks scattered on the sand. The depth of occurrence ranges from very shallow to about 10 metres. Both are rather common at a depth of about 3 metres in the intermediate zone between a gradually sloping rocky shore and the sand. Although they forage from the sand they are rarely found on open stretches. *M. lateristriga,* on the other hand, lives in very shallow muddy bays and forages from the open sediment-rich substrate.

Breeding

Males of the Lateristriga Nkhata in breeding colours were seen in May and June, and those of the Makanjila Longnose between May and December, but both forms may breed the year round. Spawning takes place in the intermediate habitat where males stake out a territory and build a semicircular sand-castle nest against a small rock, a so-called "cave-crater nest". Territorial males can be as near to one another as 150 cm. Mouthbrooding females retreat among the rocks, and aquarium observations indicate that they care for their offspring for the first few days after first release.

Both long-nosed forms are ideal aquarium residents because of the attractive coloration of the males, which is exhibited almost all year round, their relatively small size, and their rather peaceful behaviour towards other tankmates.

References

ECCLES, D.H. & TREWAVAS, E. (1989) Malawian cichlid fishes. The classification of some haplochromine genera. Lake Fish Movies, Herten, Germany.
JACKSON, P.B.N. (1961) Check-list of the fishes of Nyasaland. Occ. Pap. Nat. Mus. S. Rhod., 25B: 535-621.

Sexual Selection in Lake Malaŵi Cichlids

Jay R. Stauffer, Jr.[1] and Karen A. Kellogg[1]

The ichthyofauna of Lake Malaŵi, Africa, represents an extreme case of explosive speciation with over 460 described species and possibly another 500 to 1000 undescribed ones, which are thought to have arisen within the last two million years. The number of fish species in Lake Malaŵi exceeds the total number of freshwater fish species throughout the entire North American continent. Isolating the causes of such tremendous diversity has been the focus of numerous evolutionary studies. Certainly, intralacustrine geographic isolation has been shown to be a major force in large scale faunal diversification, but physical segregation alone does not sufficiently account for the interspecific variation that occurs over the fine spatial scales observed in Lake Malaŵi. Models of sexual selection appear to be a plausible explanation for the rapid speciation within seemingly non-delimited communities.

Historically, sexual selection has been employed to explain such seemingly detrimental characteristics as the peacock's tail, the widow bird's long tail-feathers, and the ornamental breeding sites of the bower bird. The frequently conflicting forces of natural and sexual selection were first noticed by Darwin (1871). Natural selection arises from differential viability and fertility, while sexual selection results from competition for mates. Sexual selection can move mean male character values

1. A sand-dwelling male defending the bower that he has constructed.

skew the distribution of male reproductive success. Fisher (1930) was the first to propose a runaway process, which could result from assortative mating. Essentially, the selection process is accelerated because both the male character and the female preference for this character are selected simultaneously. Dominey (1984) was the first to discuss the importance of sexual selection in relation to rapid speciation of African cichlids, and stated that these cichlids possess many of the characteristics needed for sexual selection. The purpose of this paper is to summarize the characteristics of several Lake Malaŵi cichlid species, which are indicative of sexual selection.

The shallow-water cichlids in Lake Malaŵi can be divided into two major ecological groups: the rock-dwelling species (mbuna) and those which live over the sand. Fishes in both ecological groups aggregate and defend territories, particularly during the peak breeding seasons. This congregation of reproductively active males is often

far from the equilibria that would preside under natural selection alone (Kirkpatrick and Ryan, 1991). In essence, female preference can strongly

[1]School of Forest Resources, The Pennsylvania State University, University Park, PA 16802, U.S.A.

referred to as a lek. The territories within a sand-dweller lek typically consist of a sandcastle structure which is termed a "bower", whereas the mbuna defend a rocky cave. Neither type of territory offers much in the way of protection, food, or any other resource to females — it is simply used as a mating site, hence the term "bower" instead of "nest" for the sand-dweller sand structures. In addition, all of the endemic cichlids of Lake Malaŵi are maternal mouthbrooders. The eggs of almost all these species are actually fertilized inside the mother's mouth, and she will carry the developing embryos until they are free-swimming fry. The development cycle of the fry takes an average of two weeks, during which time the female refrains from eating. Each cichlid embryo is therefore much more costly for females than for males, thus creating a system that is ripe for sexual se-

lection by female choice. Theoretically, females should be much more selective in picking their mates because each embryo requires a large physical investment, whereas males should mate with as many females as possible to recover the costs of their territory defence.

In order for sexual selection by female choice to be fully operational, females must be free to make mate selections. The lekking system of the cichlids provides an excellent forum for female mate selection. A female can readily survey many different males and drop down into the territories of only those males of interest. Behavioural observations indicate that females are completely free to investigate numerous males with no interference or corralling-type behaviour from the territory residents. Furthermore, it is frequently observed that females will actually engage in circular courtship with males, only to exit the territory prior to egg-laying. In fact, in a recent study we found that females of one sand-dwelling species will visit an average of ten different males before finally laying eggs with a mate they find suitable (Stauffer *et. al.*, in prep.). Moreover, based on behavioural as well as molecular data, it is typical for a female to choose several mates to fertilize a single brood of eggs (Kellogg *et al.*, 1995, McKaye, 1991). The fact that females are able to mate with several males is also indicative of free female choice.

Another criterion that is inherent in all sexual selection models is that males must experience differential reproductive success. There must be some variation in male characteristics by which females can make mating choices, which in turn gives rise to the different fitness levels among the males. There are two obvious classes of characteristics in the cichlid breeding system that have been evaluated for their role in female choice: bowers in the sand-dwelling communities (Fig. 1, on the previous page) and body coloration in the rock-dwellers (Figs. 2, 3, and 4).

Research on the breeding behaviour of several Lake Malaŵi sand-dwelling fishes has demonstrated that the process by which females choose mates is complex. McKaye *et al.* (1990) found a preference for larger bowers in female *Copadichromis conophorus*. This species forms huge leks that may contain more than 50,000 males at the height of the breeding season (McKaye, 1984, 1983). In comparisons between pairs of bowers, males on larger bowers received a 2- to 3-fold increase in female attention (bower entry and circling behaviour) over males on smaller bowers. In a smaller lek, occupied by 20 to 50 *Otopharynx*

argyrosoma males, individuals occupying bowers closest to the centre of the lek received approximately three times as many matings per male as those around the periphery (McKaye, 1991; Fig. 5). On a third, multi-specific lek, occupied primarily by *Lethrinops cf. parvidens* (approximately 150 individuals), we found that both bower height and location within the lek were important (Stauffer *et al.*, in prep). In order to separate the effects of bower size and bower location, we substituted artificial bowers in the lek. During the 3-5 hours per day of underwater observations, several tagged males on small bowers (< 8 cm high), fertilized no eggs throughout a three week period, during which approximately 1800 eggs were laid on other bowers in the lek. We replaced these small bowers with tall (22 cm) tin bowers that we covered with sand (Fig. 6, next page). The same tagged males were observed fertilizing between 15 and 30 eggs per day when occupying these artificial bowers (Stauffer *et al.*, in prep). *Lethrinops auritus* males build bowers that consist of a single central sand mound surrounded by several smaller sand "bumps". *Lethrinops auritus* females preferred to mate with males whose bowers contained more peripheral bumps (Stauffer *et al.*, 1995).

Studies of female choice among the rock-dwelling cichlids are somewhat sparse, simply due to the limitations on direct observation in the field for this group. The final stages of mating occur out-of-sight within the rocky caves of the mbuna, making positive paternal identification difficult. Although breakthroughs in molecular techniques (DNA fingerprinting) are helping to remedy the problems associated with mbuna observations, we have turned to laboratory studies to critically evaluate the role of coloration in mate selection. In a series of studies that are currently under way in our laboratory, we are making use of computer-animated male models (for animation examples see the Internet at http://cac.psu .edu/~gho/Vis_Group.html). By using this type of technology we can control extemporaneous variables such as courtship patterns, male size, pheromones, and pharyngeal bone grinding, therefore isolating the effects of male body coloration. There has been only one other study that dealt specifically with male body coloration in the mbuna. Hert (1991) examined the effects of egg-

spot numbers on the reproductive success of male *Pseudotropheus aurora*. Egg-spots are conspicuous yellow or orange blotches on the anal fin of many cichlid species. These intense spots of colour look remarkably similar to the eggs of cichlids. It has been observed that during courtship the males spread their anal fins against the surface on which the eggs are being deposited by the female. The female attempts to pick up the "eggs" and in doing so actually takes sperm into her mouth. Hert (1991) found that males with greater numbers of egg-spots experienced greater reproductive success.

The studies of female choice in Lake Malaŵi cichlids have focused primarily on how or, more

2. *Pseudotropheus barlowi* at Mbenji Island.
3. *Ps. aurora* at Likoma Island.
4. *Ps. callainos* at Nkhata Bay.
5. Bar graph of the number of eggs *Otopharynx argyrosoma* males fertilized in a lek in the Cape Maclear National Park.

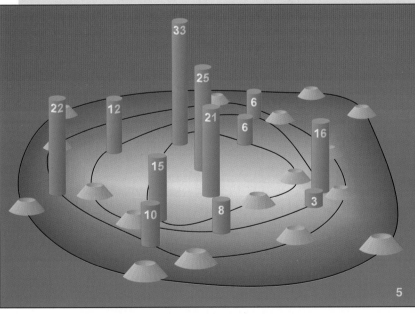

specifically, what criteria they use. Perhaps the more interesting question, but also the more difficult to answer, is why do females bother making what are undeniably costly decisions. Mate selection is a time-, and therefore, energy-consuming process which exposes individuals to potential predators. The most obvious answer to this ultimate question is that females make the additional effort to evaluate potential mates to avoid wasting valuable gametes by engaging in interspecific matings. Bower form, courtship behaviour, and body coloration have all been identified as species-specific characteristics. In Lake

Malaŵi ten major bower forms, varying in size from small depressions in the sand to elaborate castles, have been identified (McKaye 1991). Within each class of bower shape, significant quantitative variation in bower dimensions occurs. For example, we have demonstrated that

three closely related species in the *Copadichromis eucinostomus* group have differently shaped bowers, and have used these data to aid in the differentiation of these species. Similarly, McKaye *et al.* (1993) studied five leks of *Tramitichromis* near Nankumba Peninsula in Lake Malaŵi and demonstrated significant differences in bower shape between these leks. The environmental conditions across the three *Copadichromis* and the five *Tramitichromis* leks appeared homogeneous. We therefore regard differences in bower shape as a manifestation of a behavioural characteristic which is congruent with taxonomic delineations. In both studies the taxonomic groupings derived by differences in bower shape were also supported by morphological characters. Furthermore the *Tramitichromis* delineations were supported by genetic evidence.

Preliminary evidence indicates that members of different genera also exhibit different courtship dances. Male *Copadichromis conophorus*, *C. cyclicos*, and *C. thinos* all exhibit circular courtship patterns. Sympatric *Tramitichromis* species exhibit a figure-of-eight courtship pattern and the taxa closely allied to *T. praeorbitalis* have an S-shaped courtship dance. Thus differences in courtship dances may be as important as bower form in species recognition.

Within the rock-dwelling group, body coloration must inevitably aid in species recognition. Many populations differ only in body coloration and this has long been recognized as a delimiting characteristic among species (Stauffer and

Hert, 1992; Stauffer, 1988) (Figs. 2, 3, and 4). Several different colour morphs may occur sympatrically on the same rocky outcropping, and conversely, similar colour morphs may occur allopatrically, thus making it difficult to define taxonomic categories. In Dominey's (1984) original arguments for the prevalence of sexual selection among the cichlids of Lake Malaŵi, he argued for female choice between male colour variants. He believed that this circumstance could lead to a rapid divergence of male body coloration for which there is some evidence (Fernald and Hirata, 1979; Greenwood, 1965).

Species cues such as bower form, courtship behaviour, and body coloration seem nearly failure-proof in the field. There have been only a handful of documented hybridizations in Lake Malaŵi. This is utterly amazing given that there are over 1,000 species from which to choose a mate. At least two cases of hybridization in the lake are believed to be the result of translocation. The first example is based on nine specimens found at Thumbi West Island which are believed to be of intergeneric hybrid origin (Stauffer *et al.*, 1996). The hybrids are a cross between *Cynotilapia afra*, a species that was translocated from the northern part of the lake approximately 20 years ago, and *Pseudotropheus zebra*, a similarly coloured species native to Thumbi West Island in southern Lake Malaŵi. These two species are naturally sympatric in other locations throughout the northern region of the lake; yet Thumbi West Island is the only site where we have found specimens representing possible hybridization (Figs. 7, 8, and 9). The second case of suspected hybridization was also found off Thumbi West Island, and again believed to be the result of a translocation. Several specimens that appeared to be a hybrid between *P. zebra* BB and *P. callainos* were video-taped at this locality. Finally, observations made while diving off Thumbi West Island indicate that an introduced member of the *Pseudotropheus tropheops* group maybe hybridizing with a "native" species.

Although the avoidance of interspecific matings may be the ultimate reason for mate selection, there appears to be more to the story. The evidence gathered from field studies of sand-dwelling leks and the laboratory studies of rock-dwellers indicates that males experience differential reproductive success when competing against conspecifics for mates. So why, once a female has narrowed her prospects down to the correct species, would she invest still more energy in mate selection? In a recent review

Kirkpatrick and Ryan (1991) classified models of female-choice selection according to whether selection on preferences was direct or indirect. They concluded that in many species preferences evolve in response to direct selection on female fitness. For example, female *Otopharynx argyrosoma* may select males that defend bowers in the centre of the lek in an attempt to avoid the egg predators that are often seen circling breeding arenas. Hert's (1991) demonstration that females select males with higher numbers of eggspots could be the result of greater spawning stimulation and synchronisation, which in turn could lead to the reduced risk of brooding unfertilized eggs.

Several models can be classified as invoking indirect sexual selection on female preferences. In the "good genes" models, female preference is derived from the improved fitness of a female's progeny because of genes acquired from the male. One such model postulates that females prefer males carrying genes that make them resistant to parasites (Hamilton and Zuk, 1982). These so-called "non-adaptive" models postulate that female preference is not related to the forces of natural selection acting on the population. Fisher (1930) was the first to propose a "runaway" process, which has since been extensively modelled (O'Donald, 1980; Lande, 1981; Kirkpatrick, 1982) and discussed (Arnold, 1983; Kirkpatrick, 1987). One feature of the non-adaptive models is that the runaway process can be initiated by arbitrary female preferences, and several recent studies have shown that female preference for particular male characters can evolve long before the characters themselves. Preferences may frequently arise from sensory biases (Ryan and Keddy-Hector, 1992) and may be an inherent property of sensory systems (Enquist and Arak, 1993). Kirkpatrick and Ryan (1991) interpret this to mean that direct, rather than indirect, selection was responsible for the evolution of female preferences. Ryan and Rand (1993) have stressed the importance of recognizing that sexual selection and

6. The artificial bowers that were placed on a *Lethrinops cf. parvidens* lek.
7. *Pseudotropheus cf. zebra* off Thumbi West Island.
8. *Pseudotropheus cf. zebra* x *Cynotilapia cf. afra* hybrid off Thumbi West Island.
9. *Cynotilapia cf. afra* off Thumbi West Island.
Photos by Dr. Jay Stauffer.

species recognition are elements of a single process: the matching of male signal traits to female preference function.

The intriguing question that arises as the result of most sexual selection models is what has been coined "the paradox of the lek". Strong selection caused by mate choice is likely to deplete genetic variation in the male traits preferred by females. The paradox is then, why do females show strong discrimination in lek species if the genetic benefits of choice are so small (Borgia, 1979)? It is interesting that multiple paternity is prevalent in Lake Malaŵi cichlids (Kellogg *et al.*, 1995). We hypothesize that females mate with multiple males in an attempt to avoid egg predators or as a means of bet-hedging. We have also observed that females will simply drop down into several bowers on the periphery of the lek as they are leaving the breeding arena (Stauffer *et al.*, in prep). Regardless of the reason, multiple matings may provide adequate variation within the population so that it behoves a female to be choosy about the majority of her matings.

References cited

ARNOLD, S. J. (1983). Sexual selection: the interface of theory and empiricism. In: Bateson, P, (ed.). *Mate choice.* Cambridge University Press, Cambridge, Massachusetts.

DARWIN, C. (1871). *The descent of man and selection in relation to sex.* John Murray, London.

DOMINEY, W. J. (1984). Effects of sexual selection and life history on speciation: species flocks in African cichlids and Hawaiian *Drosophila*. In: Echelle, A. A. & I. Kornfield, (eds.). *Evolution of fish species flocks.* University of Maine Press, Orono, Maine.

ENQUIST, M. & A. ARAK (1993). Selection of exaggerated male traits by female aesthetic senses. *Nature*, 361:446-448.

FERNALD, R. D. & N. R. HIRATA (1977). Field study of *Haplochromis burtoni*: habits and co-habitants. *Env. Biol. Fish.*, 2: 299-308.

FISHER, R. A. (1930). *The genetical theory of natural selection.* Dover, New York.

GREENWOOD, P. H. (1991). The cichlid fishes of Lake Nabugabo, Uganda. *Bull. Br. Mus. Nat. Hist. Zool.*, 12: 315-357.

HAMILTON, W. D. & M. ZUK (1982). Heritable true fitness and bright birds: a role for parasites? *Science*, 218: 384-387.

HERT, E. (1991). Female choice based on egg-spots in *Pseudotropheus aurora* Burgess 1976, a rock-dwelling cichlid of Lake Malawi, Africa. *J. Fish Biol.*, 38: 951-953.

KELLOGG, K. A., J. A. MARKERT, J. R. STAUFFER, Jr., & T. D. KOCHER (1995). Quantifying multiple paternity in Lake Malawi cichlid fish. *Proc. Roy. Zool. Soc. London Ser. B.*, 260: 79-84.

KIRKPATRICK, M. & M. J. RYAN (1991). The evolution of mating preferences and the paradox of the lek. *Nature*, 350: 33-38.

KIRKPATRICK, M. (1987). Sexual selection by female choice in polygynous animals. *Ann. Rev. Ecol. Syst.*, 18: 43-70.

KIRKPATRICK, M. (1982). Sexual selection and the evolution of female choice. *Evol.*, 36: 1-12.

LANDE, R. (1981). Models of speciation by sexual selection on polygenic traits. *Proc. Nat. Acad. Sci. USA*, 78: 3721-3725.

McKAYE, K. R., J. H. HOWARD, J. R. STAUFFER, Jr., R. P. MORGAN II, & F. SHONHIWA (1993). Sexual selection and genetic relationships of a sibling species complex of bower building cichlids in Lake Malawi, Africa. *Jap. J. Icht.*, 40: 15-21.

McKAYE, K. R., S. M. LOUDA, & J. R. STAUFFER, Jr. (1990). Bower size and male reproductive success in a cichlid fish lek. *Amer. Nat.*, 135: 597-613.

McKAYE, K. R. (1991). Sexual selection and the evolution of the cichlid fishes of Lake Malawi, Africa. In: Keenleyside, M. H. A., (ed.). *Cichlid fishes: behaviour, ecology and evolution.* Chapman and Hall, London.

McKAYE, K. R. (1984). Behavioural aspects of cichlid reproductive strategies: patterns of territoriality and brood defence in Central American substratum spawners versus African mouth brooders. In: Wooton, R. J. & G. W. Potts, (eds.). *Fish reproduction: strategies and tactics.* Academic Press, New York.

McKAYE, K. R. (1983). Ecology and breeding behavior of a cichlid fish, *Cyrtocara eucinostomus*, on a large lek in Lake Malawi, Africa. *Env. Biol. Fish.*, 8: 81-96.

O'DONALD, C. E. (1980). Genetic models of sexual selection. Cambridge University Press, Cambridge, Massachusetts.

RYAN, M. J. & A. S. RAND (1993). Species recognition and sexual selection as a unitary problem in animal communication. *Evol.*, 47: 647-657.

RYAN, M. J. & A.L. KEDDY-HECTOR (1992). Directional patterns of female mate choice and the role of sensory biases. *Amer. Nat.*, 139: S4-S35.

STAUFFER, J. R., Jr., N. J. BOWERS, K. R. McKAYE, & T. D. KOCHER (1995). Evolutionary significant units among cichlid fishes: the role of behavioral studies. *Amer. Fish. Soc.*, Symposium 17: 227-244.

STAUFFER, J. R., Jr., N. J. BOWERS, T. D. KOCHER, & K. R. McKAYE (1996). Evidence of hybridization between *Cynotilapia afra* and *Pseudotropheus zebra* (Teleostei: Cichlidae) following an intralacustrine translocation in Lake Malaŵi. *Copeia*, 1996: 203-208.

STAUFFER, J. R., Jr. & E. HERT (1992). *Pseudotropheus callainos*, a new species of mbuna (Cichlidae), with analyses of changes associated with two intra-lacustrine transplantations in Lake Malawi, Africa. *Ichth. Explor. Freshwaters*, 3: 253-264.

STAUFFER, J. R. (1988). Descriptions of three rock-dwelling cichlids (Teleostei: Cichlidae) from Lake Malawi, Africa. *Copeia*, 1988: 663-668.

A new *Lethrinops* with a peculiar bower

Ad Konings

The genus *Lethrinops* comprises many different species which all are sand-dwellers, or at least are rarely found in rocky habitats. However, during breeding most inshore species are found near a rocky coast or have centred their breeding arenas near distinctive objects on the bottom, often a single rock or a tree trunk which has been washed into the lake via a river. Of course such objects are unable to give protection and may thus serve solely as landmarks. At depths of 10 to 20 metres the water can at times be quite turbid, in particular above a sandy or muddy bottom; a dark object is then easier to locate because it stands out against the suspended sediment in the water and the similarly-coloured substrate. So if territorial males know the position of their territory relative to such an object, they can quickly locate their domain when they return from, for example, a long chase (egg-robbers are sometimes chased over a very long distance) or a foraging period.

Lethrinops females, meanwhile, seem to be attracted to the shape and size of the male's "bower" (nest) rather than his coloration (see Stauffer & Kellogg on page 23). We therefore see a rather wide interspecific variation in bower structure but not so much in male breeding col-

our. At some locations three to five different *Lethrinops* species may have overlapping breeding arenas yet the males of the different species may all have a very similar breeding colour. Females are nevertheless able to recognise their correct partner because of the shape of his bower. That males of some species go to considerable lengths to attract the correct breeding partner was first demonstrated by Lewis (1980), who reported on the remarkable spawning sites built by *Lethrinops auritus* males. *L. auritus* is a small species, growing not much longer than 10 cm, which is normally found in very shallow water over muddy bottoms. The male's bower consists of several heaps of mud/sand, 10-15 cm high, which are arranged into a circle with a diameter of about 100 cm. Another heap, usually consisting of sand and a little taller than the rest, is piled up at the centre of the circle. A small pit — the actual spawning dish — is dug alongside this central heap. Because such elaborate bowers are built in very shallow water (2-5 metres of depth) *L. auritus* is found in sheltered bays where the

Lethrinops sp. "auritus lion", male at Lion's Cove (T'hoto), Malaŵi.

wind and waves have a less destructive power. Nevertheless the breeding arena I was able to observe at Cape Maclear (August, 1993) suffered noticeably from wave action and *L. auritus* males spent most of the day rebuilding their "court-yards".

Over the years I have found several other *Lethrinops* species in which males construct elaborate bowers (Konings, 1995), and the photos on this page show some of their peculiar constructions. Recently (May, 1995) I found another small *Lethrinops* species, dubbed *L.* sp. "auritus lion", in the narrow bay at Lion's Cove. Unfortunately I saw only a single male who had built his territory on the sand at a depth of about 25 metres. The bower consisted of several heaps of sand which were, however, not placed in a circle. The heaps were about 15 cm tall and sited 50 to 80 cm apart. It was early morning and the bay is so narrow that sunlight cannot penetrate to this depth until about noon. I was able to photograph the attractively coloured male, but whether other males of the same species would construct similar breeding sites could not be confirmed.

Another small *Lethrinops* species, *L.* sp. "nyassae", does not build its own bower but adopts varying structures abandoned by other species. So it is possible that that single male *L.* sp. "auritus lion" "inherited" his heaps of sand from another species. The coloration of the male Auratus Lion is rather different from that of other known *Lethrinops* species, so in fact they would not necessarily need to indulge in energy-consuming bower construction in order to indicate to females that they were different from similarly coloured males breeding in the same area. The male's coloration resembles that of a *Nyassachromis* species, and it was only after a while (remember, the light was rather dim), when I saw the male feeding from the sand, that I realised that it was a member of the genus *Lethrinops*. It may therefore build an unusual bower in order to be distinguishable from *Nyassachromis* species as well, because all known species of the latter genus build sandcastles on the sand. Time will tell, but not before more individuals of this attractive sand-dweller are found and observed.

References

KONINGS, A. (1995) *Malawi cichlids in their natural habitat. 2nd edition.* Cichlid Press, St. Leon-Rot, Germany.

LEWIS, D.S.C. (1980) The nest pattern of *Lethrinops aurita* Regan, a cichlid fish from Lake Malawi. *J. Sci. Tech. Malawi* 1(1), pp 36-37.

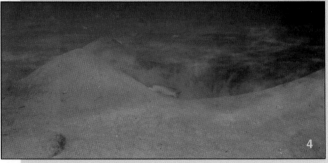

The bower of *Lethrinops auritus* (5) consists of a circle of heaps of sand and mud, and a central cone where spawning takes place (1). That of *Lethrinops* sp. "auritus lion" lacks the central spawning cone (2). The bower of *Lethrinops* sp. "longimanus likoma" (6) is a shallow spawning dish surrounded by small heaps of sand and mud (3). *Lethrinops* sp. "longipinnis ntekete" (7) is, with a maximum size of about 20 cm, much larger than the previous three species which have a maximum total length of about 10 cm. Its bower is a very large crater, the rim of which is "ornated" with large heaps of sand.

The "Silver Torpedo" — an unusual cichlid

Peter Baasch

In December 1994 I realised a long-standing ambition when I obtained several "silver torpedos" from Stuart Grant. The available information on these fishes is limited to the fact that in Autumn they can be seen over the flat sandy bottom in Senga Bay, where the local people fish for them with rod and line. The hypothesis that they come to this area to breed remains unproven, as none of the specimens so far examined has been carrying eggs (Grant, pers. comm.).

The silver torpedo must be regarded as a delicate, easily stressed species, which responds badly to capture and transportation. This must be taken into account when establishing them in the aquarium: sudden movements in (eg during maintenance) or near the aquarium are likely to send them into a panic, and they may even jump out of the tank. They nevertheless quickly adjust to their new surroundings and, once settled, lose their shyness completely.

The silver torpedo is a slender and extremely elongate cichlid, whose body shape is reminiscent of *Nyassachromis*, but three times as long: ultimate size can be up to 25 or 30 cm. In well-fed specimens the dorsal and ventral profiles are almost mirror-images of each other, and it then becomes clear that the trivial name "torpedo" was aptly chosen. The relatively small head is moderately pointed; the large eyes are sited very close to the upper head profile; the mouth is terminal, rather small, and pointed. In dominant individuals the anal fin and the posterior portion of the very elevated dorsal are sometimes developed into a long point, extending back to the caudal base and beyond.

1

The basic pattern is more readily seen in juveniles than in older specimens, and is more distinct on the posterior half of the body. There is a pattern of elongate spots overlaying the barely visible mid-lateral band; the shortest lies on the caudal peduncle and is about the same length as the latter, becoming wider on the base of the tail. The second is about twice as long and ends shortly before the caudal spot.

The pigmentation on the anterior part of the body is not as distinct. I get the impression that it consists of two elongate spots beginning just

A male (1) and a female (2) "Silver Torpedo" from Senga Bay, Malaŵi.
Photos by Ad Konings.

behind the operculum. The lower of these two spots lies right on the lower lateral line, and there is a pigmented area running parallel to it, on the upper lateral line. It looks as if the two spots are connected by an "X". I think I can detect a similar pattern in *Lethrinops* and its allies. Perhaps this anterior pigmentation should in fact be regarded as a single, poorly delineated, spot centred on the upper lateral band, in which case there is also a faintly-marked, curved, diagonal band. A further row of spots runs along the base of the dorsal.

Females are somewhat smaller than males and normally silver in colour, although once they have adjusted to aquarium life they become rather darker (flesh-coloured) and develop yellow fins with iridescent dots in the dorsal. It is difficult to remain objective in describing the coloration of males: the entire fish, apart from the bluish head, is a rhapsody in light blue with yellow, gold, or orange highlights. The anal fin is ornamented with a large number of orange-coloured "egg-streaks"; the high dorsal is particularly impressive, sprinkled with specks of gold and suffused with a reddish hue under some lights. The lower fins become dark during courtship.

The form of the body, caudal peduncle, and fins all indicate an accomplished swimmer: these fishes are fast — very fast! The swimming behaviour is characteristic of an open-water species.

Interestingly these fishes, like the Utaka, normally harvest individual food items from the water, or pick them from the substrate like *Protomelas* species. They do not, however, take in any sand in the process. Over a period of time algae may develop on the substrate, and not long afterwards the fishes may pick up some sand while feeding from the bottom — perhaps a case of rapid adaptation! Juvenile fishes introduced into the aquarium remain unmolested, so we can rule out a predatory lifestyle.

The preliminaries to spawning last for more than a week. Courtship is tempestuous but elegant: females are pursued only briefly, never harried, so no damage occurs. Spawning took place on the open sand between three rocks, without any preliminary "earth-moving". I was able to observe only the final stages of the spawning ritual, and gained the impression that the eggs were collected as soon as they were laid. Although the same site was chosen for three different spawnings, I am of the opinion that in the lake this species spawns anywhere that males and females encounter one another.

The transfer of brooding females to separate quarters is fraught with difficulty, as these nervous fishes react badly to the move. It is advisable to wait until the 15th day and then transfer them after "lights out".

One female of about 17 cm length total length released exactly 100 very slender, 15 mm long, fry which looked more like bits of string than fishes, and had difficulty in coping with freshly-hatched *Artemia*. They grew very slowly, but soon developed yellow fins and the pattern described above. Later on I put some 4-5 cm youngsters in with the adults — who completely ignored them.

If one considers these observations as a whole, then one may well conclude that in the case of this species Mother Nature has created an anomaly, a fish that does not accord with our preconceived notion of the "Malaŵian scheme of things": the silver torpedo has the form of an out-size, predatory *Nyassachromis* combined with the colour pattern of a *Lethrinops*; it consumes the same food as *Protomelas* but using the Utaka feeding strategy; and spawns on the sand — without constructing a nest — even though it is probably an open-water species!

A real gem from the depths of Lake Malaŵi

Peter Baasch

Copadichromis sp. "virginalis gold" has been found only at Nkanda in the northernmost part of Lake Malawi on the Tanzanian shore. It was found at a depth of 36 metres and deeper, where males were seen defending cave-crater "nests" in breeding arenas (Konings, 1995).

In June 1994 I was able to obtain, via Laif DeMason in Florida, a few live specimens which were not much bigger than 4 cm total length. The body of this small utaka is laterally compressed and relatively deep. The tail and the caudal

considerably smaller than that of a similarly coloured species found in the southern part of the lake and with which it has been confused: *Copadichromis* sp. "virginalis kajose" or Gome Virginalis. The latter species can attain a total length of about 18 cm and is also found in much shallower water than the "Virginalis Gold".

Female *C.* sp. "virginalis gold" become almost as large as males, and since they have a fuller body they sometimes appear even larger. The coloration of ripe males resembles that of male *Aulonocara maylandi*. The entire body is

dark brown to black; from the tip of the snout to the upper edge of the tail, and running along the dorsal part of the body, there is a golden yellow band. Excited males exhibit black bars superimposed on the dark body. The anal fin, which is a very dark colour, is adorned with 5 to 7 "egg-spots" which are arranged like a string of pearls on the edge of the fin.

Because of the depth at which this utaka has been found, I have reduced the light over the tank and mixed some black gravel with the fine sand I use as substrate. Furthermore I have placed a few stones in the tank, forming caves which are frequently used as shelter by males as well as females. In the aquarium males construct small spawning pits, often using the cover of a cave created by rocks. The spawning crater is not perfectly round and normally includes part of the stones

peduncle are strongly built. The head is pointed and the small mouth is angled somewhat upward. The maximum total length of this species may be no more than about 10 cm which is

which give it protection. This type of nest resembles those seen in the lake. As far as I was able to deduce from my observations of the spawning, which took place mostly inside the "cave", the eggs are taken up immediately by the female and thus probably fertilised inside her mouth. A 5 to 6 cm long female released only 8 fry after a three week incubation period.

If care is taken regarding water quality, the Virginalis Gold is a problem-free aquarium fish which exhibits very peaceful behaviour. I have kept several males together in a relatively small tank (100 cm long) and although some of them exhibited breeding coloration simultaneously, no serious problems arose. Juveniles of the first spawn were kept together with the adult breeding group and no harm was done to them either. I have not tried to keep *C.* sp. "virginalis gold" with other cichlids, as experience with other species of the *virginalis*-group has taught me that they are not bold enough to stand up against most other species.

1. An adult male *Copadichromis* sp. "virginalis gold" in the author's aquarium.
2. The female sometimes appears larger than the male because she has a fuller body and a spotless silvery colour.
3. *Copadichromis* sp. "virginalis kajose" (at Gome, Malaŵi) is frequently confused with the "Virginalis Gold", but is a much larger species which lives in shallow water.
4. A territorial male *C.* sp. "virginalis gold" at Nkanda, Tanzania.
Photos by Ad Konings.

OTHER AFRICAN CICHLIDS

Polychromatism in rock dwelling Lake Victoria cichlids: types, distribution, and observations on their genetics

Ole Seehausen[1] & Niels Bouton[1]

Introduction

Polychromatism or colour polymorphism in cichlids has long been subject to discussion but not much progress has been made towards an understanding of the phenomenon and its evolutionary implications. In this article we propose to make a few observations, illustrated by a series of colour photographs, regarding types and frequencies of polychromatism, their taxonomic distribution, and the genetics underlying them.

At the time when Fryer & Iles published their milestone book on East African cichlids (1972), it was thought that polychromatism was a common phenomenon among the mouthbrooding haplochromine cichlids of the East African Great Lakes. In their account two types of polychromatism can be distinguished. One of these, apparently more or less restricted to females, and at that time known from Lakes Victoria, Kivu, and Malaŵi, involves so-called "bicolor" and "orange-blotched" morphs as opposed to "normal" ones. For convenience we will call this type A polychromatism. The second involves male nuptial coloration and is seen only in males, and was recorded from Lakes Malaŵi (*Pseudotropheus zebra*, *Ps. tropheops*, *Petrotilapia tridentiger*) and Victoria (*Haplochromis obesus*). We will refer to this as type B polychromatism. In the years after the publication of Fryer & Iles' book it was found that many of their examples of type B polychromatism in cichlids of the Mbuna group in Lake Malaŵi in fact represented reproductively isolated sibling species rather than colour morphs (Holzberg 1978, Marsh *et al.*, 1983). Subsequent work on Lake Victoria cichlids has demonstrated that anatomically very similar forms, which can be told apart in the field only by differences in male coloration, differ ecologically (Hoogerhoud *et al.*, 1983, Goldschmidt *et al.*, 1990), and is in line with Holzberg's and Marsh's results (though evidence for assortative mating is lacking). In reviewing more recent works such as these, Greenwood

[1]Institute of Evolutionary and Ecological Sciences, Section Ecology and Section Morphology, Leiden University, P.O. Box 9516, 2300 RA Leiden, Netherlands.

1. Facing page: Bicolor female of *H.* "blue scraper" from Makobe Island, Lake Victoria.
2. Bicolor male of *H.* "blue scraper" from Makobe Island.
All photos by Ole Seehausen.

(1991) came to the conclusion that there are not many unequivocal examples of intrapopulational male polychromatism, most of those recorded now being known to have been based on errors of taxonomy, and that the phenomenon is usually confined to females. This conclusion brings with it important implications for the interpretation of the role of polychromatism in the speciation process. Coloration is thought to play an important role in the mate recognition system of cichlids (Dominey, 1984) and it is conceivable that polychromatism connected with non-random mating could lead to a splitting of gene pools and to speciation in micro-allopatry or sympatry (Maynard Smith, 1966; Turner & Burrows, 1995). Polychromatism restricted to females, however, is unlikely to have such an effect on gene pools in animals with a polygynous mating system in which females are thought to play the major part in mate selection. The observations on rock-dwelling Lake Victoria cichlids presented below, however, suggest that polychromatism generally, and male polychromatism in particular, is more common than hitherto believed.

Methods

During ecological field research on rock-dwelling haplochromines in south-eastern Lake Victoria between 1991 and 1995, each colour phenotype encountered among more than 10,000 individuals of more than 100 species was photographed. For species definition a combination of a rather small number of morphological, coloration, and ecological criteria was applied.

Morphological criteria were body depth, head length, length and length/width ratio of snout and lower jaw, shape and arrangement of buccal and pharyngeal teeth. Coloration criteria were body and fin coloration as well as melanin patterns of females and males. Ecological criteria were patterns of micro-distribution. Sympatric forms identical in micro-spatial distribution and morphology were considered conspecific even if they differed in coloration; differently coloured forms that exhibited differences in either micro-distribution or morphology were considered to represent separate species. The definition of allopatric forms is less unequivocal, but of no great relevance here since we define the phenomenon of polymorphism as one of coexisting forms in one population (Kosswig, 1965) and not as variation among geographically isolated populations. This method of species recognition is similar to that applied by Ribbink (1986) and Witte & Witte Maas (1987), but we must emphasize that none of these classes of criteria is alone sufficient to delimit species.

In a number of populations, which were ecologically studied in some detail and over several years, it was possible to determine morph frequency. Sampling was performed with gill nets on the surface of the rock substrate and in the water column above it, and by angling in the crevices between the rocks and in rock pools. Some rather anecdotal but nevertheless informative observations on the inheritance of polymorphism were made on two polymorphic populations of two species that were kept and bred in the laboratory primarily for other purposes.

Results

1. The frequency of polychromatism in rock-dwelling haplochromines

Discontinuous polymorphism was recorded in 16 of 81 species, ie in about 20%. Species where less than five individuals were collected are excluded from this statistic. Continuous variation, producing phenotypical differences of a magnitude comparable to those among discontinuous morphs, was recorded in a further five species and is included in the following account of poly-

Table 1. The frequency of colour polymorphism in the five most speciose trophic groups of rock-dwelling haplochromines. Sample size (n) = number of species studied

	discon. polym.	contin. var.	total	polym. with >2 morphs	n
insect & plankton eaters	8.6%	8.6%	17%	3%	35
snail shellers	44%	—	44%	22%	9
snail crushers	25%	—	25%	—	4
epilithic scrapers	30%	9%	39%	13%	23
epiphytic scrapers	—	—	—	—	5

morphism for the reasons outlined below. Table 1 shows the frequency of polymorphism in the five major trophic groups of rock-dwelling cichlids.

2. Types of polychromatism and their distribution over species groups

Five kinds of polychromatism have been observed. Following the terminology introduced earlier, the first two described below are type A polychromatism, and the other three type B polychromatism.

Bicolor/normal polymorphism. Bicolor morphs exhibit a variable pattern of black blotches on a white or light yellow background and are also referred to as piebald morphs (Figs. 1-3). This kind of polymorphism is discontinuous, according to field data. It was recorded from six species: *Haplochromis (Paralabidochromis) chilotes, H. (P.) chromogynos, Macropleurodus bicolor, H. (Ptyochromis) sauvagei, H. "blue scraper"* and *H. "velvet black"*. Greenwood (1956a) found it in *Hoplotilapia retrodens* which occurred in our samples from rocky habitats but is extremely rare following the Nile perch upsurge. *H. retrodens* and the first four of the species listed above represent four of the five genera in one division of the *Psammochromis-Macropleurodus* lineage defined by Greenwood (1980)

on the basis of morphological criteria and confirmed by Dorit (1990) with molecular data. The remaining two belong to Greenwood's *Neochromis* lineage. Bicolor morphs were encountered more often in females than in males, but bicolor males have been found in *M. bicolor* (Greenwood, 1956a; pers. obs.), *H. retrodens* (Greenwood, 1956a), *Ptyochromis sauvagei* (Seehausen, 1993), and *H. "blue scraper"* (pers. obs., Fig. 2). Greenwood (1959) found all females of *H. (P.) chromogynos* to be of the bicolor morph, but we found mainly normal-coloured females of this or a very similar species. Greenwood (1956b) reported one bicolor individual of *H. (Neochromis) nigricans*. We have never found any but know that those of the morphologically very similar *H. "blue scraper"* can be mistaken for *H. (N.) nigricans*.

OB/normal polymorphism. OB (orange blotched) morphs, as defined herein, differ from bicolor morphs mainly by having the black blotches on pink to bright orange background (Figs. 4, 5, 14) or, in the case of *H. "copper black"*, having orange blotches on a "normal" ground (Fig. 6). Completely orange and orange-red individuals occur as well. According to field data, this type of polymorphism, like the bicolor/normal, is discontinuous. Populations can, however, be variable as regards the background colour which can range from pink to deep red. OB/normal polymorphism was recorded from five species: *H. "blue scraper"*, *H. "velvet black"*, *H. "unicuspid scraper"*, *H. "copper black"* and *H. (Lipochromis) cf. melanopterus*. The first four are *Neochromis/Xystichromis*-like epilithic algae scrapers (Seehausen, 1994). OB morphs have been recorded in *Hoplotilapia retrodens*, once again by Greenwood (1956a) and also by Witte & Witte-Maas (pers. comm.). In most of these species OB morphs were encountered more often in females than males, but OB males were found in *H. "blue scraper"*, *H. "velvet black"* and *H. "copper black"*. In the case of the latter the OB morph was in fact found exclusively in males, but with an exceptionally low frequency (1 out of 2012 and 1 out of 1000 individuals at Makobe and Chamagati Islands respectively).

3. Bicolor female of *Haplochromis* (*Paralabido-chromis*) *chilotes*.
4. OB ("peppered") female of *H*. "velvet black".
5. OB male of *H*. "blue scraper" from Makobe Island.
6. OB male of H. "copper black".

7-10). According to field data, variation between the two morphs can be continuous. This kind of polymorphism was recorded from nine species: *H. nyererei* (continuous), *H.* "big blue", *H. (Ptyochromis) sauvagei*, *H.* "deep water rock sheller", *H.* "stone", *H.* "pseudoblue", *H.* "blue scraper" (continuous), *H.* "velvet black", *H.* "short scraper". The first two belong to the *H. nyererei* group (Seehausen, 1996); the next two to the *Psammochromis-Macropleurodus* lineage; *H.* "stone" is a snail crusher similar to the *Labrochromis* lineage; *H.* "pseudoblue" a planktivore of the *H.* "pseudonigricans"-group; and the last three are algae scrapers of the *Neochromis* lineage.

Blue/black polymorphism. One morph is more or less bright blue, the other black (Figs. 11, 12). According to field data, variation between the morphs can be continuous. This polymorphism was recorded from four species, all members of the *Neochromis* lineage: *H.* "blue scraper", *H.* "unicuspid scraper", *H.* "giant scraper" and *H.* "velvet black". A similar polymorphism was described by Greenwood (1959) for *H. (Lipochromis) obesus*.

Anal-fin-colour polymorphism. The morphs vary in their anal fin colour, which is bright yellow

7. Yellow male of *H.* "blue scraper" from Makobe Island.
8. Blue male of *H.* "blue scraper" from Makobe Island.
9. Red male of *H.* "stone" from Python Island.
10. Blue male of *H.* "stone" from Python Island.
11. Blue male of *H.* "unicuspid scraper" from Igombe Island.
12. Black male of *H.* "unicuspid scraper" from Igombe Island.

The size, number, and distribution of blotches of dark pigment in bicolor and OB morphs are variable. In both morphs individuals occur with only small dots of dark pigment. Such fishes are commonly referred to as "peppered" and are sometimes regarded as a distinct morph (Greenwood, 1967; Fryer & Iles, 1972).

Yellow-red/blue polymorphism. In species exhibiting this kind of polymorphism one morph is predominantly blue or grey-blue, and the other yellow, yellow with a red chest, yellow with a red dorsum, or predominantly red (Figs.

or orange in one morph, bright red in a second, and black in a third. Two or three of these morphs can occur in a population. According to field data, variation between the morphs can be continuous. This polymorphism was recorded from four species, three of which have the body almost entirely black: *H.* "black and orange" (*H. nyererei*-group), *H.* "black pseudonigricans", *H.* "pseudonigricans" (both *H.* "pseudonigricans"-group). The fourth one, *H.* "yellow anal scraper", is a bluish algae scraper (*Neochromis* lineage).

3. Frequency of phenotypes

Bicolor and OB polymorphism was in most cases found in both sexes. With one exception it occurred with higher frequency in females than in males (table

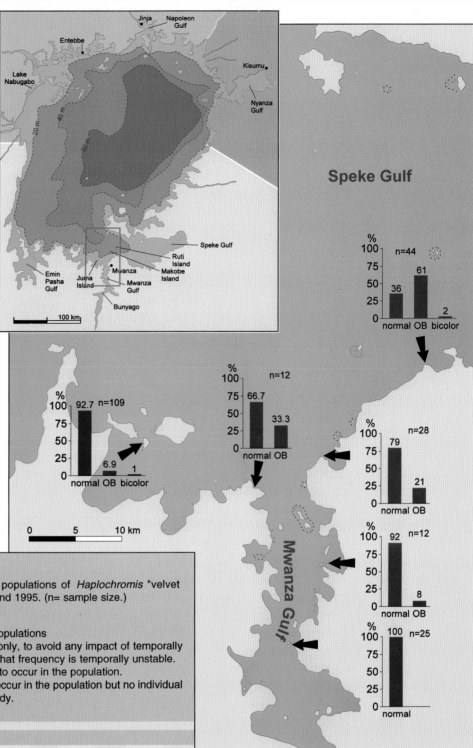

13. Map showing the frequency of three colour morphs among females of six populations of *Haplochromis* "velvet black", based on samples from 1993 and 1995. (n= sample size.)

Table 2. Phenotype frequency in some populations
Based on samples from 1993 and 1995 only, to avoid any impact of temporally asymmetric sampling, since we suspect that frequency is temporally unstable.
— indicates that the morph is not known to occur in the population.
0.0 indicates that the morph is known to occur in the population but no individual of the particular sex was found in this study.
Sample size (n) = number of individuals

males

	blue	black	yellow	OB	bicolor	n
H. "blue scraper" Makobe Island	93%	0.3%	5%	1%	0.5%	680
H. "unicuspid scraper" Igombe Island	43%	57%	—	0.0	—	12
H. "velvet black" Igombe Island	2%	98%	0.0	0.0	0.0	41
H. "velvet black" Bwiru	3%	94%	3%	0.0	—	35
H. "velvet black" Anchor Island	—	100%	0.0	0.0	—	11
H. sauvagei Igombe Island	62.5%	—	37.5%	—	0.0	16
H. "stone" Python Island	54%	—	46%	—	—	13
H. "pseudoblue" Python Island	70%	—	30%	—	—	30

females

	"normal"	OB	bicolor	n
H. "blue scraper" Makobe Island	38%	35%	27%	146
H. "unicuspid scraper" Igombe Island	60%	40%	—	5
H. "velvet black" Igombe Island	37%	61%	2%	44
H. "velvet black" Bwiru	79%	21%	—	28
H. "velvet black" Anchor Island	92%	8%	—	12

2). Bicolor and OB polymorphism was found to be often, but not always, characterized by a low frequency of the bicolor or OB morphs. The highest frequency measured was 61% in females of *H.* "velvet black" at Igombe Island and 34.9% in females and 1.1% in males of *H.* "blue scraper" at Makobe Island. One of the lowest measured incidences was 0.05% in males of *H.* "copper black", also at Makobe Island (possibly representing a case of recurrent

14

mutation). Large differences in frequency were also found between populations of the same species (Fig. 13). There is a strong tendency for bicolor and OB morphs to be more frequent at places with higher water transparency.

The yellow-red/blue, blue/black, and anal-fin-colour polymorphism are often characterized by abundant occurrence of both morphs, more commonly in the case of the first type than with the last two. Some examples are given (table 2).

4. *Observations on the genetics of polymorphism*

Discontinuous polychromatism is usually thought to be determined by a single Mendelian factor, ie one gene with several alleles (eg Maynard Smith, 1993). If the relationship between the alleles is one of simple dominance, offspring from a cross between two morphs will always resemble the parental stock (one parent in the F_1, both grandparents in the Mendelian 3:1 ratio in the F_2). Like previous authors we found type A polychromatism to be distinctly discontinuous in natural populations. The well-studied *H.* "blue scraper" of Makobe Island (Speke Gulf), which has been the subject of ecological research for several years, is a typical example. The discontinuity was also present in the first generations of laboratory stocks derived from pairings of blue males with normal and OB females. Males were all blue, females were of either typical OB or normal appearance (Figs. 14, 15). In the second generation, however, differences between the morphs became continuous and at least five classes of phenotype could be distinguished (Figs. 16-19). The frequency of the phenotypes, in nature distinctly bimodal, approached the normal distribution and "pure" OB and normal morphs became rare (Fig. 21).

The parental stock of the captive population of *H.* "blue scraper" was composed of more than 10 fishes. All the males were blue, the females either "normal" or OB. In the F_2 generations yellow, black, and OB males appeared alongside blue males and intermediates, and females were "normal", OB, or intermediate. Bicolor morphs never occurred, so apparently none of the breeding fishes among the parental stock was heterozygous for bicolor coloration, while some were for yellow and black male coloration. Likewise the OB morph never occurred in a laboratory stock of *H.* "velvet black" from Anchor Island, originating from crosses between black males and normal females, while in the wild 8% of the females are OB. By contrast, yellow males, which have never been found in this population in nature, occurred as early as the F_1 laboratory generation.

Discussion

With about a quarter of the haplochromine species from the rocky shores of southeastern Lake Victoria being polychromatic, the frequency of polychromatism among them is much higher than was previously thought (Snoeks *et al.*, 1989; Greenwood, 1991; Snoeks, 1994, 1995) and is very similar to that found among Lake Kivu haplochromines (Snoeks, 1994, 1995). Two new kinds of type B polychromatism (male nuptial polychromatism) are described, and for one, already observed by Greenwood (1959: blue/black polymorphism), new examples are given. With the new data it becomes apparent that male polychromatism is a frequent phenomenon among rock-dwelling Lake Victoria cichlids. Males of 22% of the species are polychromatic and as many as five male colour morphs have been found to exist in a single population (Figs. 2, 5, 7, 8). This is in marked contrast to previous observations, and is unexpected if, as has been assumed, male coloration is a major factor in mate recognition. Thus polychromatism, as a potential source for speciation, is certainly not rare. An interesting observation in this regard is that the colour phenotypes characterizing the yellow-red/blue type of polymorphism are also commonly observed in haplochromine sibling species in Lakes Victoria (Hoogerhoud & Witte 1981) and Malaŵi (Holzberg, 1978; Konings, 1989, for colour photographs), one species being yellow or red, and its sibling blue. It is conceivable that such sibling species are derived from formerly incompletely isolated colour morphs of a single species. Two scenarios have been suggested in which reproduction barriers can evolve between colour morphs of one species: in sympatry, through morph assortative mating, or in allopatry, through genetic drift or locally different selection regimes leading to fixation of alternative alleles in different populations (eg Maynard Smith, 1993). The latter of these mechanisms appears to be particularly effective in small and well-isolated populations like those of rock-dwelling haplochromines (Dorit, 1990): populations just a few kilometres apart exhibit significant differences in colour morph frequency (see table 2, and figure 13 for populations of *H.* "velvet black").

The distribution of polymorphism across the species appears not to be random. Polychromatism is clearly commoner in some groups than in others. This is apparent at the

ecological group level: snail shellers and epilithic scrapers are clearly more often polychromatic than are insect/plankton eaters and epiphytic scrapers. The correlation between the types of polychromatism and presumed phylogenetic groups is even more apparent: type A polychromatism is significantly more common in species of the *Psammochromis-Macropleurodus* lineage (oral shellers and some insectivores) and species of the *Neochromis* lineage (epilithic algae scrapers) than in other groups. In the former bicolor/normal polymorphism dominates, occurring in all polychromatic species, some of which have OB morphs alongside bicolor morphs. In the second lineage it is precisely the other way round. These patterns seem non-random, but their interpretation is difficult because similar kinds of type A polychromatism also exist

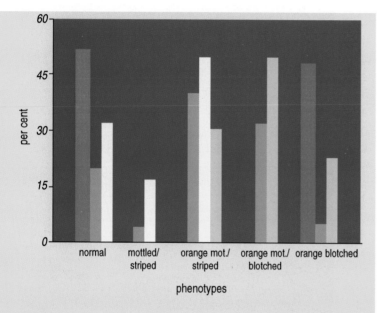

per cent

phenotypes

Fig. 21. The frequency of two colour morphs ("normal" and "orange blotched") and their intermediates among females in the natural population of H. "blue scraper" at Makobe Island (red bars) and in three F_2 laboratory broods (blue, yellow, and magenta bars). The bicolor morph in the natural population is not considered. Abbreviations: orange mot. = mottled on orange ground colour.

in very different species of the open waters of Lakes Victoria and Kivu (Fryer & Iles, 1972; Snoeks, 1994), in Mbuna of Lake Malaŵi, and even in the tilapiine *Oreochromis variabilis*. Type B polychromatism seems less strongly associated with phylogenetic groups.

The difference between discontinuous polychromatism and continuous variation is thought to lie in the genetics determining the observed variability. Discontinuous polymorphism is thought to be determined by a single Mendelian factor, ie by variation at one locus (alleles of a single gene); continuous variation by alleles of a number of genes

with additive effects (eg Maynard Smith, 1993). While field observations on the frequency of colour morphs in haplochromine cichlids suggest that discrimination between these two phenomena is possible, data derived from laboratory stocks cast doubt on this. We cannot see how allelic variation at a single locus could explain the observed phenotype segregation. The observations suggest the underlying genetics are more complicated. The absence of intermediate phenotypes in the F_1 and their occurrence in the F_2 (at least five classes of phenotype, normal distribution of phenotype frequency) can most simply be explained by a three-gene model with dominance of one allele and additive gene effects. It seems to us that either a three (or more) gene model or a model with several alleles of different potency of a suppressor gene (cf. Fryer & Iles, 1972), might be needed to explain the observed patterns. In any case these laboratory observations suggest that, as regards the genetic background, the difference between discontinuous polychromatism and continuous variation in natural populations of haplochromine cichlids in Lake Victoria is less real than field observations appear to imply. Hence our decision to treat them together under polychromatism.

One implication of these observations is that discontinuity in colour variation in natural populations must, in cases like that of *H.* "blue scraper" at Makobe Island, be due to disruptive selection favouring extreme phenotypes. This can be either natural selection against intermediate phenotypes or positive morph assortative mating, ie sexual selection in favour of extreme phenotypes. This interpretation of the observations is supported by the fact that intermediate phenotypes in several cases of what is believed to be discontinuous type A polychromatism have occasionally been observed in nature (Greenwood, 1956a: *Hoplotilapia retrodens*; Fryer & Iles, 1972: *Oreochromis variabilis*; pers. obs.: *Macropleurodus bicolor, H.* "velvet black", and *H.* "blue scraper", Fig. 20).

A separate line of evidence in favour of non-random mating among some colour morphs can be derived from the laboratory observations on the occurrence in filial generations of morphs not present in the parental stock. Type B morphs not represented among the parental stock frequently occurred among the offspring. The occurrence in nature of such morphs may be kept low by stabilizing selection against the rare morph. Type A morphs not represented among the parents, by contrast, never occurred among the offspring. This suggests that few normal-coloured fish are heterozygous in this respect, while heterozygosity for type B polymorphism seems common. In our view this in turn suggests that gene flow between type A morphs is restricted in nature. An unambiguous demonstration of this would be strong evidence for sympatric speciation through a phase of balanced colour polymorphism. Although it is essential to guard against unjustified "splitting" of taxa, it is possible that in a few cases we still underestimate species numbers as a result of the "lumping" together of reproductively isolated colour morphs, as was formerly done (and may still be, in some cases — see Konings, 1995) in Lake Malaŵi. We are, however, of the opinion that such instances are rare among rock-dwelling Lake Victoria cichlids, and insufficient to invalidate our arguments on male polychromatism. Underwater field research on the mating behaviour of Lake Victoria cichlids in their natural habitat is needed to resolve this problem.

Acknowledgements

We would like to thank the Government of the Republic of Tanzania (Prof. Dr. Bwathondi, Tanzania Fisheries Research Institute) for granting us the necessary research permits to carry out the work on Lake Victoria, Dr. Frans Witte (University of Leiden), Dr. Erik Verheyen (Royal Belgian Inst. of Natural Sciences), and Dr. Jos Snoeks (Africa Museum, Tervuren) for comments on the manuscript.

References

DOMINEY, W. (1984) Effects of sexual selection and life history on speciation: species flocks in African cichlids and Hawaiian *Drosophila*. In: Echelle, A.A. & I. Kornfield (eds). *Evolution of fish species flocks*. University of Maine Press, Orono: pp 231-249.

DORIT, R.L. (1990) The correlates of high diversity in Lake Victoria haplochromine cichlids: a neontological perspective. pp 322-353 In: Ross, R.M. & W.D. Ollmon (eds). *Causes of Evolution, a Palaeontological Perspective*. University of Chicago Press, Chicago and London.

FRYER, G. & T.D. ILES (1972) *The cichlid fishes of the great lakes of Africa*. Oliver & Boyd, Edinburgh.

GOLDSCHMIDT, T., F. WITTE & J. DE VISSER (1990) Ecological segregation in zooplanktivorous haplochromine species (Pisces, Cichlidae) from Lake Victoria. *Oikos* 58; pp 343-355.

GREENWOOD, P.H. (1956a) The monotypic genera of cichlid fishes in Lake Victoria. *Bull. Br. Mus. nat. Hist. (Zool.)*, suppl. 3; pp 295-333.

GREENWOOD, P.H. (1956b) A revision of the Lake Victoria *Haplochromis* species (Pisces, Cichlidae), Part I. *Bull. Br. Mus. nat. Hist. (Zool.)*, 4; pp 223-244.

GREENWOOD, P.H. (1959) A revision of the Lake Victoria *Haplochromis* species (Pisces, Cichlidae), Part III. *Bull. Br. Mus. nat. Hist. (Zool.)*, 5; pp 179-218.

GREENWOOD, P.H. (1967) A revision of the Lake Victoria *Haplochromis* species (Pisces, Cichlidae), Part VI. *Bull. Br. Mus. nat. Hist. (Zool.)*, 15; pp 29-119.

GREENWOOD, P.H. (1980) Towards a phyletic classification of the "genus" *Haplochromis* (Pisces, Cichlidae) and related taxa. Part II: the species from Lakes Victoria, Nabugabo, Edward, George and Kivu. *Bull. Br. Mus. nat. Hist. (Zool.)*, 39; pp 1-101.

GREENWOOD, P.H. (1991) Speciation. In: Keenleyside, M.H.A. (ed). *Cichlid Fishes, Behaviour, Ecology and Evolution*. Chapman & Hall, London & New York: pp 86-102.

HOLZBERG, S. (1978) A field and laboratory study of the behavior and ecology of *Pseudotropheus zebra* (Boulenger), an endemic cichlid of Lake Malawi (Pisces, Cichlidae). *Zeitschrift für Zoologische Systematik und Evolutionsforschung* 16; pp. 171-187.

HOOGERHOUD, R.J.C. & F. WITTE (1981). Revision of species from the "*Haplochromis*" *empodisma* group. *Neth J. Zool.* 31; pp 232-273.

HOOGERHOUD, R.J.C., F. WITTE & C.D.N. BAREL (1983). The ecological differentiation of two closely resembling insectivorous haplochromine species (Cichlidae) from Lake Victoria (*H. iris* and *H. hiatus* (Pisces, Cichlidae). *Neth. J. Zool.* 33; pp 283-305.

KONINGS, A. (1989) *Malawi cichlids in their natural habitat*. Verduijn Cichlids, Zevenhuizen, Netherlands.

KONINGS, A. (1995) Remarkable observations on the Red Zebra. *The Cichlids Yearbook* 5; Cichlid Press, Germany: pp 42-47.

KOSSWIG, (1965) Genetische Grundlagen des Polymorphismus. *Zool. Anz.* 175; pp 21-50.

MARSH, A.C., A.J. RIBBINK & B.A. MARSH (1981) Sibling species complexes in sympatric populations of *Petrotilapia* Trewavas (Cichlidae, Lake Malawi). *Zool. J. Linn. Soc.* 71: pp 253-264.

MAYNARD SMITH, J. (1966) Sympatric speciation. *Amer. Nat.* 100: 637-650.

MAYNARD SMITH, J. (1993) *The theory of evolution*. Cambridge University Press, Cambridge, 354 pp.

RIBBINK, A.J. (1986) The species concept, sibling species and speciation. *Ann. Mus. Roy. Afr. Centr., Sc. Zool.*, 251; pp 109-116

SEEHAUSEN, O. (1993) Victorian Cichlids, Part II: The oral shelling/crushing molluscivores. *The Cichlids Yearbook* 3; Cichlid Press, Germany: pp 50-55.

SEEHAUSEN, O. (1994) Victorian Cichlids, Part III: The epilithic algae scrapers. *The Cichlids Yearbook* 4; Cichlid Press, Germany: pp 42-51.

SEEHAUSEN, O. (1996) Distribution of, and reproductive isolation among colour morphs of a rock-dwelling Lake Victoria cichlid (*Haplochromis nyererei*). *Ecol. Freshw. Fish.* (in press)

SNOEKS, J. (1994) The haplochromine fishes (Teleostei, Cichlidae) of Lake Kivu, East Africa: a taxonomic revision with notes on their ecology. *Ann. Mus. Roy. Afr. Centr. Sc. Zool.* 270: 221pp.

SNOEKS, J. (1995). Polychromatism in Lake Kivu haplochromines: two for the price of one? *The Cichlids Yearbook* 5; Cichlid Press, Germany: pp 48-53.

SNOEKS, J., E. COENEN, L. DE VOS & D.F.E. THYS VAN DEN AUDENAERDE (1989) Genetic polychromatism in Lake Kivu haplochromines. *Ann. Mus. Roy. Afr. Centr., Sc. Zool.*, 257: pp 101-104.

TURNER, G.T. & M.T. BURROWS (1995) A model of sympatric speciation by sexual selection. *Proc. R. Soc. Lond.* B 260; pp 287-292.

WITTE, F. & E.L.M. WITTE-MAAS (1987) Implications for taxonomy and functional morphology of intraspecific variation in haplochromine cichlids of Lake Victoria. In: F. Witte. *From form to fishery*. Ph.D thesis, Leiden University.

Two *Paretroplus* species

Jean-Claude Nourissat

Following our arrival on the east coast of Madagascar and our encounter with *Ptychochromis*, the second cichlid that we found was *Paretroplus polyactis*, which is still very common in the Pangalanes canal. This species grows fairly large: a length of 25 cm is possible, and Catala (1977) states that it is possible to find specimens weighing 750 or even 900 gm. Its vernacular name, phoneticised (it is spelt differently in Malagasy), is "Machvouatok".

The Pangalanes canal runs for hundreds of kilometres from north to south along the Indian Ocean coast of Madagascar, and contains brackish water, as in many places it is connected to the ocean, allowing salt water to enter the system. Both *Ptychochromis* and *Paretroplus* adapt very well to brackish water. I made numerous dives in the Ambilalelaitso area and a little further away in the Ampanotoamaizina region, but failed to find a breeding pair, despite searching

extensively, both in the Pangalanes canal itself and the adjacent marshes where the water is extremely soft. I wanted to find some juveniles, which would be easier to transport home than adults. Perhaps it was the wrong time of year (I was there in January).

Paretroplus polyactis is fairly well coloured in this part of Madagascar; it would appear that further north, in the Maroantsetra region, they are much redder. They are rather timid fishes that show little inclination to approach a diver even if, like me, he remains motionless on the

bottom. In the clear waters of the Pangalenes canal one can see them patrolling in small bands of 5 or 6 individuals, foraging in the substrate — they are bottom-sifters which pick up a mouthful of sand, extract anything edible, and then eject all the sand via their gills. This species is the most highly prized of all Malagasy fishes as regards culinary value. Its flesh is like that of a sole, pink (rather like the colour of salmon), and quite delicious, and everyone who had had the chance to taste it told us that this was a truly extraordinary fish. I haven't tried it myself, not having caught it in sufficiently large numbers.

Catala (1977) has studied this species, and shared his observations with us, commenting that he had never managed to get this fish to breed in the artificial lake near his home; although he had frequently seen them breeding in the rivers they had always refused point blank to reproduce in semi-captivity. I have no experience of keeping and breeding them in the aquarium, having failed to keep alive the 3 or 4 individuals which survived the journey home.

When planning our researches into the other cichlids of the genus *Paretroplus*, the only reference work available was Kiener & Maugé (1966), which we absorbed to the full. The authors provide maps of the geographical localities for the various Malagasy cichlids, and 4 species of *Paretroplus* are said to inhabit the northwest region. Local conditions have, however, changed considerably since they were there — the tilapia invasion has changed everything — but it was this area that we needed to visit in order to try and rediscover the native cichlids. We were completely independent, thanks to the 4-wheel-drive we had rented in Tananarive, and we visited all the rivers and lakes along the road which runs as far as Majunga, a distance of a little over 500 km. Crocodiles are common all over the island, and there is no question of diving willy-nilly without first consulting the local people. In order to minimise the danger our preferred method of fishing was with a cast net.

But time and again, all along the route from Tananarive to Majunga, we found numerous lakes and marshes where we caught nothing but tilapias. It is quite incredible how these fishes have invaded everything — lakes, rivers, and streams. Their young grow faster than those of the native Malagasy cichlids and they have completely overwhelmed the latter to the point where they have completely disappeared from the majority of lakes where they were formerly very numerous.

A large nature reserve has been established in the forest of Ankarafantsika, near to the town of Tsaramantroso. We stopped at the forestry station and were able to visit a small lake, with reasonably clear water, close to the road. Fishing is forbidden there except with rod and line, but we were able to get special permission to use our cast net, and were lucky enough to catch two new cichlids which we had never met before: *Paretroplus maculatus* and *P. kieneri*. We had to catch more than 100 tilapias to get one *Paretroplus*, but we persisted, and were rewarded with several of the latter.

The first year we visited this lake the largest specimens we caught measured no more than 10 cm. They had the large black mid-lateral spot characteristic of the genus, and were easy to transport as there was no problem with lack of oxygen due to overpopulation of the container!

We had already seen a few specimens in the market at Tananarive. All the fishes caught for food in Madagascar are dried in the sun or over wood-fires, making it possible to transport them to the point of sale — there is no electricity in the countryside or the villages, only in the towns, and there are no refrigerators and even less refrigerated transport. By making a few enquiries in the market we learned that these *Paretroplus maculatus* came from the Maevatanana region, where they still inhabit the lakes in the area, which, however, we had not fished.

The next year, during our second trip, we caught numerous large *Paretroplus* in the lake near Tsaramandroso. It must have been the breeding season (it was October), as on several occasions we caught two large adults together in the cast net, and they were exhibiting the black throat which appears to be their nuptial coloration. Because of the crocodiles, very much in

evidence in this lake and which had attacked someone not long before, it goes without saying that our diving masks remained in the car. We were unable to catch any juveniles, but as I write there are some 8-10 *Paretroplus maculatus* swimming around in my aquarium, although I have not so far managed to breed them. I have seen ovipositors protruding on several occasions, but without any further developments.

Finally, a note on coloration. There is considerable variation in the colour pattern of these fishes: sub-adults commonly exhibit dark verti-

1. *Paretroplus polyactis*, a freshly caught specimen.
2. A beautiful specimen of *P. maculatus* in the aquarium.
Photos by Jean-Claude Nourissat.

cal bars, but these seem to disappear completely in large specimens. The lyre-shaped tail, bordered with red, is very similar to that of *P. petiti* and *P.* sp. "red tail". A beautiful and elegantly-shaped fish, whose colours are, however, rather unassuming.

References

CATALA, R. (1977) Poissons d'eau douce de Madagascar. *Rev. fr. Aquariol.* 1; pp 27-32.
KIENER, A & M. MAUGÉ (1966) Contribution à l'étude systématique et écologique des poissons Cichlidae endémiques de Madagascar. *Mem. Mus. Natl. Hist. Nat.* 40(2); pp 51-99.

Oxylapia polli, the enigmatic cichlid of the Nosivolo River

Patrick de Rham

Oxylapia polli was described as a new genus and new species by Kiener and Maugé in 1966. The type locality of the species, first collected in 1963, is the Nosivolo River at Marolambo, situated approximately 170 km to the south-east of the capital city of Tananarive. The Nosivolo is a right bank tributary of the Mangoro, the largest river of Madagascar's eastern slope.

In February 1989, two ichthyologists working in the USA, Peter Reinthal and Melanie Stiassny, managed to reach Marolambo by land. They were able to collect 12 native species of fish, including a fair number of *O. polli* specimens. However, the most remarkable result of their trip was the discovery of a new cichlid species belonging to the previously monotypic genus *Ptychochromoides* (species description in preparation; Stiassny, pers. comm.). This was also the first cichlid species to be added in recent times to the list of 9 recorded by Kiener and Maugé in their 1966 work. The reason this easy-to-collect cichlid has not been discovered before, at least at

Fisherman casting a net in the Nosivolo River. Photo by Patrick de Rham.

the same time as *Oxylapia*, remains a mystery.

In October 1994, following an abortive overland attempt a year earlier, Jean-Claude Nourissat and I finally made it from Tana to Marolambo in a small mission plane, an airstrip having been recently completed close to this isolated little town (Nourissat, 1995). Before landing the plane circled above Marolambo and we were

briefly able to admire the beautiful and interesting landscape. The dark Nosivolo River, strewn with rocks, was shining in the sun. Stretches of calm water alternated with numerous rapids. We could see another river which tumbled down huge falls before joining the Nosivolo. The surrounding mountainous landscape was green, an indication of the prevailing wet climate, but even from the air we could see that low scrub had totally replaced the original forest.

We were very well received by the local authorities and with their help were able to muster a small team of fishermen. While they were getting ready, we went down to the river below the old colonial *Résidence* in which we had been lodged, where we found some people fishing with cast nets. After only a few minutes we were presented with our first "Katria", the local name for the new *Ptychochromoides* species discovered by Reinthal and Stiassny. We were slightly disappointed at the lack of colour in these fishes, but after this early success we felt confident that the other Nosivolo cichlid, the curious *Oxylapia polli*, now our main target, would shortly be collected. Soon afterwards our fishing team arrived and we were taken by pickup to a beautiful place some 4 km downstream, where the river runs through a succession of falls and rock-fringed pools.

Our fishermen eagerly began to cast their nets and were soon back with dozens of Katria. Leaving aside the unavoidable exotic tilapias (*Oreochromis* sp.), they caught also several "Filelabato" (literally: stone-lickers, two goby species, *Chonophorus* cf. *macrorynchus* and *Sicyopterus* sp.) and one "Sindrano", *Agonostomus telfairi*, a very interesting specialised freshwater mullet, endemic to the fast-flowing waters of Madagascar's east coast and Réunion Island. But no *Oxylapia*. What puzzled us was that in spite of our repeated efforts to describe and even sketch an *Oxylapia*, the fishermen could not understand what other more or less katria-like fish we were so eager to obtain. Unfortunately we didn't know the native name of the fish and had no photo with us. The afternoon came to an end and we had to return to Marolambo.

Back at the *Résidence*, we felt slightly dispirited. Melanie Stiassny had told me that *O. polli* was

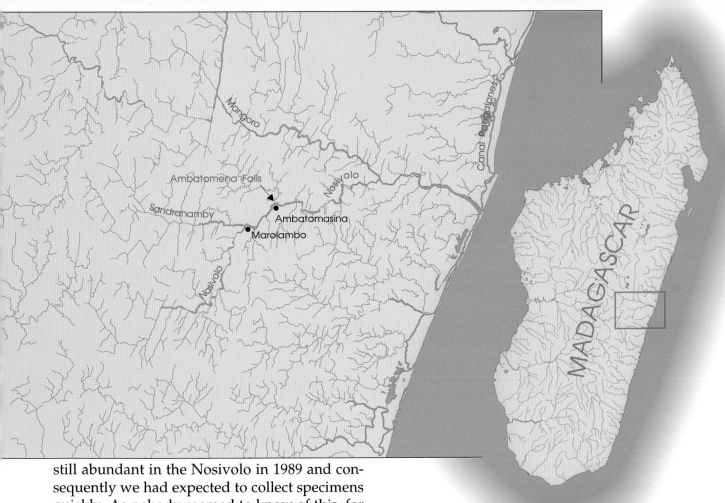

still abundant in the Nosivolo in 1989 and consequently we had expected to collect specimens quickly. As nobody seemed to know of this, for us, remarkable fish, could it be that the species had become extinct within a few years? The plane was to return the next morning to take us back to Tana, and for a while it seemed pretty certain we would not be able to collect *O. polli*. Rather vexing for two people who tended to believe they were the best cichlid collectors in the world! Our last chance was night collecting with an electric torch, but considering we hadn't seen a single *Oxylapia* during the day, we held little hope of success. Nevertheless after dinner Jean-Claude and the fishermen went a little way upstream from the village and rapids. After wading for a while in the shallow water and spotting, using his torch, several Katria and other fishes resting on the sandy bottom, Jean-Claude discovered his first *Oxylapia*. Once one had been caught, more were easily found and collected. It turned out that the fishermen knew the species well and called it "Songatana". Apparently they simply hadn't thought of the elusive Songatana! The next day we were able to take about 15 live specimens back to Tana, where, together with several Katria, they were temporarily housed in a large well equipped aquarium. Two weeks later, upon returning from a collecting trip in the South, we were appalled to learn that all our Marolambo fishes had died for no apparent rea-

son. Only one Katria survived (and is still alive today).

Thirteen months later, in November 1995, I was back in Marolambo. Unfortunately this time I was alone, as Jean-Claude, who had been very sick (most likely as a consequence of bilharzia contracted last year in Madagascar), had been obliged to stay at home. And although I now knew the native names of the local fishes and the approximate place where *Oxylapia* could be found, again met with difficulties in obtaining specimens. To start with, day fishing produced no more *Oxylapia* than last year. And although we tried night fishing, that too failed; none of my new fishermen had been with us the first time and they could not be persuaded to use the electric torch to spot the fish. I tried myself, but I am practically blind at night.... In despair I offered a large reward for live Songatana, with the result that quite a few more people went to the river with cast nets. But it was not until the evening of my last day in Marolambo that four nice Songatana were finally brought to the *Résidence*. I expected to get no more. But a little later, when it was already completely dark, a man called Jean de Dieu was introduced to me. He was holding a long-handled dip net and asked to borrow my torch. After a few hours he was back with 25 Songatana and a small "Vahona", *Ancharius brevibarbis*, a strange endemic catfish I was very keen to obtain. And later that night he collected two more Vahona and more Songatana!

About 20 *Oxylapia* and a good number of other fishes, several of which had never been brought back alive before, made it to Tananarive. But again, in spite of desperate efforts to save them, most of my Marolambo fishes died during the four days that preceded my flight back to France and Switzerland.

Eventually four Songatana were to arrive alive in Europe, two at my home in Lausanne and two, transported by a French friend, at Jean-Claud's home in southern France.

Two weeks before my visit, Oliver Lucanus, a Canadian aquarist and travelling companion of the well-known cichlid experts Paul Loiselle and Laif DeMason, had managed to reach Marolambo solo, by tractor. After collecting for a few days, he had been lucky enough to be flown out by a passing helicopter. Unfortunately he too suffered heavy losses, with most of his fishes dying even before he had left Marolambo. Only five of his *Oxylapia* eventually reached the USA alive.

Although each time the circumstances were somewhat different, these three painful and costly experiments seem to indicate that fishes from the Nosivolo River, including the two endemic cichlids, are abnormally "fragile" during the period following collecting. Katria (*Ptychochromoides* sp.) being even more delicate than *Oxylapia*. The only exception to this rule is the third cichlid species present in the area, *Paratilapia polleni*. All the specimens of "Sofony" (this species' local name) I collected in the valley (they were never found in the main channel of the river) arrived alive in Europe, confirming the already proven hardiness of this species, once widespread in Madagascar. The reason for the high initial mortality shown by most species is not known. One possible cause, currently being investigated, is mercury poisoning resulting from the washings of a mercury mine situated a few km upstream from Marolambo (Loiselle, pers. comm.). Another problem is the unusual aggressive behaviour displayed by *O. polli*, especially among their own kind. For a short time after their arrival in the USA the 5 specimens collected by Lucanus were kept in the same aquarium and the free-for-all battle that ensued left only one survivor. One of my two fishes died for the same reason.

In many ways *Oxylapia* is a strange fish. Its elongated shape and strong pelvic fins clearly indicate its rheophilous nature. However, in contrast to several rheophilous African cichlids, it has retained a functional swim bladder. For many years *Oxylapia* stood alone as the only truly rheophilous cichlid known from Madagascar. Following the discovery of the etropline "Lamena" in fast-flowing rivers of the northern centre of the island (de Rham, 1993) this is no longer the case. However, *Oxylapia* remains the island's most current-adapted cichlid.

In their natural habitat, Songatanas appear to keep to rocky areas swept by a very strong current, which is why they are practically impossible to catch with a cast net. It is only at night that

some individuals rest in shallow, quiet places. No young fishes were observed and the local fishermen were unable to tell me anything about the breeding habits of Songatana. Breeding probably takes place in the diurnal habitat of the fish, where it is practically impossible to observe. If this is so, the species must have developed special behaviour in order to be able to raise its young in turbulent fast-flowing water. This would be in marked contrast to the behaviour of Katria (*Ptychochromoides* sp.), several pairs of

1. *Oxylapia polli* in the aquarium.
2. Aerial view of the Nosivolo River near Marolambo. Photos by Patrick de Rham.

which were observed guarding their eggs (laid in a "plaque", usually on the exposed top of a rock) or young in quiet, shallow places. Incidentally, it is interesting to note that I don't remember seeing any Katria breeding in October (1994), whereas a month later in 1995 breeding pairs were common. Yet again it would appear that a Madagascan cichlid has a short and well-defined breeding period, compared to that of other, especially African, cichlids in which breeding can extend throughout most of the year. This may well be true of *Oxylapia* as well, and perhaps I just wasn't there at the right time.

O. polli is not a colourful fish. Its overall colour is grey or dull bronze, depending on the light. There is an unusual black line starting at the anterior border of the eye and running straight, horizontally, to the front. Another striking mark, apparently likewise not recorded in previous descriptions, is a dark band along the middle of the long dorsal fin. The head, and especially the mouth, of the fish are very peculiar. The bones and muscles are strong, probably relating to the feeding habits of the fish; these are not known, but Songatana could be partly insectivorous — it is very partial to bloodworm in captivity.

Up to now all *O. polli* specimens have been collected in the Nosivolo, and then only close to Marolambo. According to the local fishermen I questioned on the matter, Songatana does not extend downstream further than the Ambatomena falls (16 km from Marolambo). Upstream its range would also be limited by falls not very far from Marolambo. Songatana is not found in the Sandranamby, a large tributary which joins the Nosivolo at Marolambo, at least not above the big falls I visited during my last stay. It there-

fore seems that the species is confined to a stretch of the Nosivolo which may extend for some 40 km, but is likely to be even shorter. More recent surveys in this part of the east slope have failed to locate the species anywhere else, and therefore seem to confirm its extremely limited range.

Nevertheless, in spite of what has been said above, I personally feel it is still too early to be absolutely certain that *O. polli* is restricted to the type locality. A single glance at a map of the east slope of Madagascar is enough to indicate the complexity of the hydrographic network. Most of its numerous rivers and streams, often difficult of access, have still to be surveyed properly for fishes. A disjunct range is a possibility, and the existence of other unknown cichlid species belonging or related to *Oxylapia* should equally not be ruled out. The recent cichlid discoveries made in the much more accessible lakes and rivers of north-western Madagascar support this point. It is also worth noting that we are almost certain that the same (or a very similar) species of *Ptychochromoides* found in the Nosivolo occurs further south in a stretch of the Namorona River, above the Ranomafana Falls.

Obviously the most important and scientifically interesting enigma attached to *Oxylapia polli* concerns its phylogeny and its relationships with the other Madagascan cichlids. Melanie Stiassny, of the American Natural History Museum, New York, has undertaken detailed anatomical studies of several Madagascan cichlid species (*in* Keenleyside, 1991). The main outcome of her research is that the Madagascan cichlids, together with the three species of southern Indian cichlids of the genus *Etroplus* (closely related to Madagascar's *Paretroplus*), form a natural group that stands apart from all other known cichlids. I personally (and I think Melanie Stiassny would not disagree) would rather say "form two natural groups". The etroplines (*Paretroplus* and *Etroplus*) are obviously very special cichlids, with some specialists being inclined to consider them "para-cichlids", whereas the ptychochromines (*Ptycho-chromis*, *Ptychochromoides*, and *Paratilapia*) are without doubt true cichlids with a morphology superficially similar to some African species (eg tilapiines). However, in contrast to what was previously thought (eg by Kiener & Maugé, 1966), Stiassny stresses that the ptychochromines belong to an ancient lineage and have no close relationship with any African cichlid.

Again according to Stiassny, *Oxylapia* is unique, and may well stand in between the two Madagas-

A freshly caught juvenile *Ptychochromoides* sp. "Katria". Photo by Patrick de Rham.

can cichlid groups which outwardly appear so different from each other. She tends to believe that in spite of sharing some common characters with the ptychochromines, such as a low number of spines in the anal fin (3 in *Oxylapia* and ptychochromines, 6 or more in etroplines), *Oxylapia* shows other anatomical traits sufficient to relate it more closely to the etroplines. As Melanie Stiassny recently wrote to me: "I believe *Oxylapia* to be an etropline (although it exhibits a very interesting mix of etropline and ptychochromine characters!). It is a very odd fish and I am very interested in it."

Undoubtedly we are still far from a satisfactory understanding of the relationships of this unique cichlid. Breeding *O. polli* in the aquarium should also shed some new light. The egg morphology of *Oxylapia* can then be compared with that of other Madagascan cichlids: etropline stalked eggs are very different from those of *Ptychochromis* and *Paratilapia*. Likewise the young of the three paretropline species I have been able to observe all have a special tadpole shape and a striking con-

trasting bicolor pattern. Their behaviour is also different from that of the young of other cichlids, especially when separated from the parent fishes (Nourissat, 1993a, b, c; de Rham, 1995). Finally, the rheophilous etropline "Lamena" has shown a unique parental behaviour for a substrate spawning cichlid, with the male alone being in charge of the "health" care of the eggs and non-swimming young (de Rham, 1995). Considering all its other peculiarities, we may well expect something equally special from the parental care of Songatana.

These are some of the reasons why a few of us are determined to spare no effort to breed *O. polli* in the aquarium. At present (March 1996) there are only three live *Oxylapia* outside Madagascar, one in Lausanne (mine), one in southern France (Nourissat) and one in New York (Loiselle)! This means we need to return to Marolambo to collect and bring back alive a sufficient number of fishes, and we are already planning a joint collecting expedition to take place later this year. If and when we succeed, then back home, we will still be faced with the problem of matching compatible breeding pairs. In view of the extreme intraspecific aggression shown by the first introduced individuals, this may be not the least of the challenges offered by the enigmatic Nosivolo cichlid.

References

KIENER, A. (1972) Poissons malagasy menacés de disparition: écologie, biologie et protection de ces espèces. *In Comptes rendus Conf. Int. Cons. Nat. et Ress. Madagascar 1970.* Comm. 36; pp. 216-217. UICN, Morges, Switzerland.

KIENER, A & M. MAUGÉ (1966) Contribution à l'étude systématique et écologique des poissons Cichlidae endémiques de Madagascar. *Mem. Mus. Natl. Hist. Nat.* 40(2); pp 51-99.

NOURISSAT, J.-Cl. (1993a) Madagascar bis. *Rev. fr. Cichl.* (French Cichl. Ass.) 129; pp 8-36.

NOURISSAT, J.-Cl. (1993b) Rediscovering Madagascar: a quest for new cichlids. Part I. *Cichlid News* 2(3); pp 6-9.

NOURISSAT, J.-Cl. (1993c) Rediscovering Madagascar: a quest for new cichlids. Part II. *Cichlid News* 2(4); pp 6-11.

NOURISSAT, J.-Cl. (1995) A la recherche du Marakely à bosse — Madagascar, 1994, *Rev. fr. Cichl.* (French Cichl. Ass.) 151; pp 9-25.

RHAM, P. de, (1993) The new red cichlid from the red island. *Tropical Fish Hobbyist*, 42(2); pp 8-18.

RHAM, P. de, (1995a) Breeding the Lamena, a new cichlid from Madagascar. Part 1. *Cichlid News*, 4(1); pp 14-17.

RHAM, P. de, (1995b) Breeding the Lamena, a new cichlid from Madagascar. Part 2. *Cichlid News*, 4(2); pp 14-17.

STIASSNY, M.L.J. (1991) Phylogenetic intrarelationships of the family Cichlidae: an overview.*In* M.H.A. Keenleyside (ed.), *Cichlid Fishes, Behavior, Ecology, and Evolution*, pp.1-35. Chapman & Hall, London.

Notes on a little known cichlid from West Africa, *Sarotherodon caudomarginatus* (Boulenger, 1916), with some thoughts on the genus

Melanie L. J. Stiassny[1]

In 1983 Ethelwynn Trewavas published what can perhaps best be referred to as "the tilapiine bible". That opus, entitled *"Tilapiine Fishes of the genera Sarotherodon, Oreochromis and Danakilia"*, stands as an enduring tribute to the work of this remarkable woman. With characteristic humility, and no small touch of British understatement, Ethelwynn prefaced this truly monumental work with the observation that it was "...the result of study of African cichlid species extending over many years." Many years indeed —she began her ground-breaking studies in the 1920's, published her first paper on cichlids in 1928, and didn't stop until her death in August 1993 (see Noakes, 1994 for an account of the life and work

the first place to turn is Trewavas' *Tilapiine Fishes*. And that is exactly what I did when I returned from a collecting trip in Sierra Leone, West Africa. As part of a broad, baseline survey of the fishes of the region my colleague Peter Reinthal and I had collected alive a mixture of juvenile cichlids from the sandy shores of the Moa, a large river in the East of Sierra Leone, not far from the Liberian border. As Freyhof (1993) has already noted for readers of *The Cichlids Yearbook*, the Upper Guinean province of West Africa has a particularly rich endemic cichlid fauna, and included among my juveniles were an assortment of the "large river" Guinean endemics *Tilapia louka, T. brevimanus, Sarotherodon occidentalis, S. leonensis,* and *Tylochromis leonensis*. There were also some rather strange, elongate, silvery cichlids, each with a characteristically "horse-headed" appearance. These odd fishes, I was to learn from a careful reading of Trewavas (1983), were juvenile

Sarotherodon caudomarginatus, female with muted, non-courtship colours. Photo by Melanie Stiassny.

of Ethelwynn Trewavas). Now, I did not intend this small contribution, on a little known cichlid fish from West Africa, to be a eulogy to a former mentor, but the fish happens to be a tilapiine, and it was as "queen of the tilapias" that Ethelwynn Trewavas was so deservingly world-renowned, and hence this grateful preamble!

When confronted with an unfamiliar tilapiine,

Sarotherodon caudomarginatus (Boulenger, 1916) a poorly-known cichlid from the freshwater stretches of coastal rivers from western Guinea (River Corubal) to eastern Liberia (St. Paul River). *S. caudomarginatus* has never been studied in any detail and, according to Trewavas (1983), nothing is known of the ecology or reproductive biology of this animal.

While a similar lack of knowledge of the biology of many (the majority of?) African cichlids in their natural habitats is commonplace, I found this to be particularly galling in the case of *S. caudomarginatus*. The reason was rather simple: Ethelwynn Trewavas had produced an influential classification of tilapiines that restricted the genus *Tilapia* to the substrate-brooding species and assigned most of the mouthbrooders to the

[1] Associate Curator of Fishes, American Museum of Natural History, New York, USA.
I would like to acknowledge the many hours of hard work and meticulous observation of Lisa Mezzacappa, an undergraduate intern, who worked with me during the long hot "Summer of *Sarotherodon* Spawning", and I have borrowed much from her notes and observations.

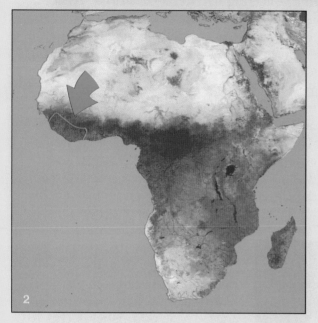

1. A typical *Oreochromis*: *O. niloticus*; collected in Hippo Pool, Lake Manyara National Park, Tanzania.
2. Distribution of *S. caudomarginatus*.
Facing page: Female *S. caudomarginatus* in typical dress when the young are released.
Photos by Melanie Stiassny.

an *Oreochromis*. A bit circular I'm afraid! Trewavas' second criterion, and the one that she felt was the more important, has to do with reproductive biology.

Remember that *Tilapia* is now restricted to include only the substrate-spawners. In these species the males and females show muted sexual differentiation, and the strong bond that forms between mated pairs extends from well before to long after spawning, and both sexes play active roles in a protracted parental care system. The tilapiine mouthbrooders are different in the following ways: in *Oreochromis* there is strong sexual dimorphism and dichromatism at breeding time. Males construct and defend "nests" (though not for hatching eggs in) in breeding arenas where they display and vie for the attention of the females which visit to spawn. No pair bond is formed, and after spawning the females leave the breeding arenas (and the males), taking their fertilized eggs away in their mouths. *Sarotherodon*, on the other hand, is far more variable in its reproductive behaviour. In the first place, as with *Tilapia*, sexual differentiation between males and females is limited. A pair bond of short duration does form prior to spawning, but after the eggs have been taken up (by the male, or sometimes by both male and female) the pair bond dissipates and the male and female go their separate ways.

So what about my *caudomarginatus*? It is West African, and by that weak criterion I supposed it was correctly assigned to *Sarotherodon*; but what of its reproductive behaviour? Well, the answer to that question was a very long time in coming. In fact it was a full four years before my *caudomarginatus* showed an interest in anything but food. However, at long last, in a large wooden community tank (2 x 1.5m) which three male and one female *caudomarginatus* shared with about seven *Paratilapia polleni*, a pair bond began to form between the large female and one of the smaller males. The pair bond was characterized by mutual tolerance and the occupation of the same areas without any hostility, while the pair grew increasingly aggressive towards the other two *caudomarginatus* males in the tank. After a few hours the pair was removed to a 500 litre (125 gallon) tank maintained at 27° C (80° F) and pH 7, and active courtship ensued.

The female, who prior to courtship had been a rather bland, yellowish grey, darkened up and developed a distinctive black blotching on her flanks. Her fins lightened from dark grey to pale with a distinctive dark edging, particularly on

genera *Sarotherodon* and *Oreochromis*. While not all tilapia aficionados agree with Trewavas, I believe that she was right and that there is strong morphological evidence in favour of the phylogenetic alignment of the mouthbrooders. However, whether or not all of the species currently placed in *Sarotherodon* (or *Oreochromis*) are each other's closest relatives, i.e. whether each genus is monophyletic, is not so easily decided. And Trewavas herself was the first to admit that the morphological distinctions between *Sarotherodon* and *Oreochromis* are minimal. Her generic assignments hinge not on anatomy but on two other criteria. The first is geographical distribution: simply stated, if a mouthbrooding tilapia is West African (but not *Oreochromis niloticus*) it is a *Sarotherodon*. On the other hand, if it is not from West Africa and is not *Sarotherodon melanotheron*, it is

the striking, emarginate caudal fin that is so characteristic of this species. Another notable feature of *caudomarginatus* during courtship was the development of bright red eyes in both sexes. Overall the male also intensified in colour, becoming considerably darker than the female with a grey-gold head, dark blotches on the flanks, and a dark chin.

As with other *Sarotherodon*, it was

clear, and that was that it was the female that was the brooding parent in this species. She was vigorously churning a batch of eggs in her mouth. Her courtship coloration was gone and she was back to a bland yellowish grey. The male was not incubating eggs, and although his coloration was somewhat subdued he retained much of the lateral blotching. The two fishes showed signs of an intact pair bond,

clearly the female that took the initiative in courtship. She persistently nipped at the male's flank while displaying with pelvic, dorsal, and anal fins erect. The male usually responded to her advances by assuming a submissive posture with his head down, body laterally deflected, and fins folded. After an initial period of active courtship, lasting about one day, female dominance subsided and both fishes actively displayed to each other and began digging in the gravel on the floor of the tank. The pair often circled and "tail-slapped", and on several occasions both male and female were observed "quivering"[2] at each other prior to performing formalized digging motions.

Spawning took place about four days after the pair was placed together. Sadly spawning was not observed, so I can't comment on the fertilization sequence. In any event, no nest or depression in the gravel was evident and it seems unlikely that either fish had excavated any sort of spawning depression. One thing, however, was

and they followed each other around the tank, occasionally brushing past one another. Although physical contact was not as frequent as during courtship, there was no hostility between them. After two days the pair, while still "peaceful", seemed to have no further interest in each other and, for fear of pending aggression, I decided to remove the male from the tank.

On the third day after spawning the eggs had hatched, that is to say the membrane surrounding the developing embryos (the chorion) had ruptured, and a number of empty chorions were floating in the tank. I examined these under a microscope in an attempt to estimate egg size, an important parameter in cichlid reproductive strategy. Each empty chorion was tear-shaped with a length of about 3.5 mm and a maximum width of about 2.5 mm, and I assume that the eggs inside the female's mouth were of similar dimensions. During the next ten or so days the female tenaciously guarded the contents of her mouth, occasionally performing digging motions in the gravel, but otherwise swimming slowly or resting on the bottom of the tank. Thirteen days after spawning the female first released her

---

[2] For readers interested in the precise meaning and significance of these and other behavioural terms I recommend a review of the chapters by Barlow, Keenleyside, and Nelissen in Keenleyside (1991).

brood. By this time she had regained the dark blotching on her flanks, as well as the bright red eyes.

This female was extremely wary of anyone in the aquarium room, and any movement outside the tank caused her to gather her shoal of twenty plus, approximately 1.2 mm, young back into her mouth (with stunning speed I might add). Interestingly, I was not to see her release her young again until 26 days later! After all that time without sight of her brood I had convinced myself that she had swallowed the whole lot. But just before I was about to reintroduce the male in an attempt to start the whole process over, I decided I would "take a peek" inside her mouth "just in case". And to my great surprise, what I found was a mouthful of healthy, horse-faced juveniles. She hadn't eaten them, she was just extremely wary about letting them out when anyone was watching! Convinced that I had now completely traumatized this already overly wary female, and fearing that she would now certainly consume her young, I removed ten of the elongate juveniles to raise *ex situ*. The remaining ten or so I put back with the female, and sat back anxiously to see what would happen. She immediately took all of them back into

1. 39 days after spawning the female was captured and her mouth opened to reveal young inside!
2. A 120-day old juvenile, removed from the female's mouth, in typical fright coloration.
3. A mouthbrooding female *S. caudomarginatus* on the left and a male in breeding coloration on the right. These fishes were collected as juveniles with a beach seine over sand at Tiwai Island, in the River Moa, Sierra Leone.
Photographs by Melanie Stiassny.

3

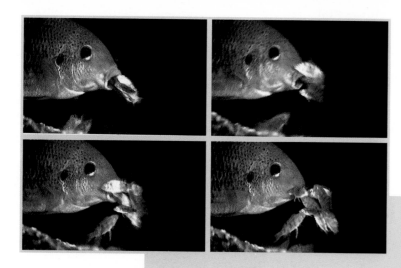

her mouth and proceeded to guard them as if they were the crown jewels.

A female *S. caudomarginatus* releasing young about 120 days after spawning.
Video sequence by Melanie Stiassny.

Over the next months (yes, *months!*) the female allowed the ten young out of her mouth with increasing frequency (the other ten, which I had placed in a small tank, were doing fine and growing apace). However, she remained wary of outsiders and always ready to take the whole brood back into her mouth whenever danger was perceived (and always at night). Interestingly, during this protracted brooding period the female was frequently observed grazing algal growths from the tank walls while she had all the young in her mouth. Such active browsing of some mouthbrooding cichlids has been reported, but only recently has it been shown that this is a means of intra-orally feeding their young (Yanagisawa & Sato, 1990). As I have indicated, the brooding of the juveniles continued for a remarkably long time. Quite amazingly it was not until the afternoon of the 137th day after spawning that the female suddenly refused to let the by now enormous young back into her mouth — even though they still seemed anxious to take refuge there!

Such a protracted period of mouthbrooding is, as far as I am aware, unprecedented, and is certainly completely unexpected in any *Sarotherodon* species. Of course, the fact that I had removed ten of her brood would certainly have "freed up" space in this female's buccal cavity, enabling her to provide accommodation for her remaining (and rapidly growing) young. However, the implications of such a behavioural flexibility (if that indeed was what I observed) are in themselves intriguing. Moreover the fact that in *caudo-*

marginatus it was the female that took an exclusive role in brooding was somewhat unexpected, as most other *Sarotherodon* species are reported to be either paternal or biparental brooders (although a female-dominated care system has been reported in one of the Cameroonian, Barombi Mbo, *Sarotherodon*).

Quite clearly there are many unsolved mysteries concerning this intriguing group of cichlids. I would, however, like to take this opportunity to repudiate the rather simplistic notion of *Sarotherodon* somehow being the intermediate between the substrate-spawning *Tilapia* and the so-called "advanced" mouthbrooding *Oreochromis*. There is no simple behavioural transition to be recognized here. However, a more interesting possibility remaining to be explored is that of the precise intra-relationships of this diverse group. If *Sarotherodon* is indeed monophyletic (and the only evidence that I have found supporting that proposition is the highly unusual and apparently invariable female initiation of courtship), then with such an array of reproductive strategies the group would seem to make an ideal model for studies of cichlid parental care strategies. On that note, I will end my thoughts on *Sarotherodon*, but I strongly urge any hobbyist with a serious interest in cichlid behaviour to consider a good look at these animals.

References cited

FREYHOF, J. (1993). *Tylochromis leonensis* Stiassny, 1989. *The Cichlids Yearbook*, 3; Cichlid Press, Germany: 60-61.
KEENLEYSIDE, M.H.A. (1991) (Ed.). *Cichlid Fishes, behaviour, ecology and evolution*. Chapman & Hall, London.
NOAKES, D.L.G. (1994). The life and work of Ethelwynn Trewavas: beyond the focus on tilapiine cichlids. *Environmental Biology of Fishes*, 41: 33-49.
TREWAVAS, E. (1983). *Tilapiine fishes of the genera* Sarotherodon, Oreochromis *and* Danakilia. British Museum of Natural History, London.
YANAGISAWA, Y. & SATO, T. (1990). Active browsing by mouthbrooding females of *Tropheus duboisi* and *Tropheus moorii* (Cichlidae) to feed their young and/or themselves. *Environmental Biology of Fishes*, 27: 43-50.

CENTRAL AMERICAN CICHLIDS

A collecting expedition to Honduras — part one

Ross. B. Socolof

It was the Spring of 1973. With three talented and compatible collecting companions I was on my way to the east coast of (then Spanish) Honduras. Dr. Albert Klee (then editor of *The Aquarium* Magazine), the late Russell Norris (who lived in Belize and was that country's foremost (only) hobbyist), Dr Harry Specht (a killifish expert and life long fish addict), and the author (who has by now lived long enough to know what not to do). In the three previous years this same team had "done" British Honduras (now Belize). Those trips had introduced to the hobby many new cichlasomines such as *Nandopsis salvini*, *Amphilophus robertsoni*, *Chuco intermedius*, *C. godmani*, *Thorichthys aureus*, *Paratheraps synspilum*, *P. melanurus*, *Vieja maculicauda*, and *Petenia splendida* (both red and normal forms).

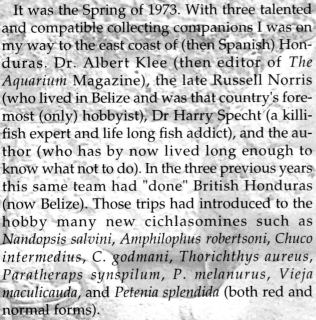

The eastern hundred or so miles between La Ceiba and Trujillo along the Caribbean coast in Honduras had not been thoroughly collected. Dr Robert R. Miller of the University of Michigan had suggested that we could find worthwhile "new" fishes in this area. He also needed additional preserved material of an undescribed "Molly" (*Poecilia* sp.). We could collect this new spot-tailed molly for him to help along the formal description process. We did get him sufficient material, so the description of this new fish could proceed, but it hasn't been completed yet (1996), 23 years since our contribution! I have no idea when the first specimens were found. This, of course, is not the fault of Dr Miller, but it does illustrate the way high priority work takes precedence.

Al, Harry, and I were on a plane for San Pedro Sula, Honduras, that stopped in Belize, where Russ was first in line to board. We four were in San Pedro Sula an hour later. As soon as we cleared customs we went through a public health check. We presented our health certificates. At this point Dr Specht, who is a physician and actually programmed or gave us our shots, was still fumbling about for his certificate. He then discovered that he had neglected to bring it along! It was not a lengthy delay — they had a rusty old needle full of dysentery germs ready for people like him. He got shots all over again.

Russ was now busy checking out local aeroplanes and pilots to make arrangements for a rental for at least two days. We hired a pilot with a 6 passenger, red Cessna 206, at a cost of $60.00 an hour for flying time. The waiting time on the ground was $7.50 per hour. I sure do miss "the good old days". We flew a local line to La Ceiba where we found a clean motel. The pilot would fly into La Ceiba at 9.00 am to pick us up. At the airport we had rented a Datsun. We had a very late lunch/dinner (orange Fanta and eggs), unpacked, and planned the next day's collecting. In the morning we discovered that there was no restaurant at the motel. We followed the desk clerk's suggestion, got lost, and ended up in a large shed about a block away, where breakfast was being served to lots of people. We had no idea where we were and what was going on. We sat down and were immediately served fruit, two hard fried and rubbery eggs, refried beans, burnt toast, and unbelievably strong black coffee. About then someone discovered us. Everyone got upset as we were definitely not members of the agricultural workforce whose commissary we had gatecrashed. They did allow us to pay. By the time we had finished charming them they made us a big sack of sandwiches for the trip. We ate breakfast there every day.

During the next two days we made four collections using the red Cessna. We flew south along the coast at about two thousand feet, heading for the Mosquito coast and the province of Gracias a Dios. We then understood why the pilot picked us up later than we wanted. He had to wait to let the early morning fog and smoke from the burning "milpas" (Mayan Indian corn plots) burn off from the low range of mountains that runs along the east coast. The first landing was made in a rough cow pasture alongside the Río Sico about ten kilometres south of Iriona on the coast. That was our only easy landing. We worked hard but collected very few interesting fishes for our efforts. Nothing new except a different molly (*Poecilia* species) with horizontal rows of black spots along the sides, one spot per scale. The cichlids included *V. maculicauda*, *Archocentrus spilurus*, *Amphilophus robertsoni*, *N. friedrichsthalii*, and *N. managuensis*.

Our second landing was on a rough field above the Río Patuca near the town of Sipul. A fast-moving boulder-strewn river made any collecting difficult. Mostly a waste of time. We worked hard and collected only eight species of fishes which included *N. managuensis*, *A. spilurus*, *V. maculicauda*, and *A. robertsoni*.

The third landing was at the Río Coco (also called Río Segovia) near Auasbila. This was a better spot. The landing was terrible. We never found the airstrip that was supposed to be there, and the pilot instead landed on the exposed (dry season) bank which was covered with smallish-looking rocks. If he had known how bad it was, he said, he would never have made the attempt. The smallish-looking rocks turned into boulders (up to 12 inches across) as we touched down. We were semi-hysterical (fright!) as we repeatedly bounced back into the air trying to land. It was luck, not skill, that kept the plane from major dis-

aster. For the next few hours the pilot spent his time picking up big rocks to give himself a fighting chance of getting airborne again.

We needed to unwind. It was the "silly season" so we held the first annual Honduran discus competition. We did not have a discus so we bent the rules a bit. We used the dried "meadow muffins" (cow flops) that were conveniently laid out on the banks. Klee and Specht tied for first, proving that they could throw the furthest. When Klee was told he had won he replied "suckahatch". None of us had ever heard such an obscene and blood-curdling curse. Almost afraid to find out, we asked what evil curse he had put on our heads. He then unravelled the "suckahatch" secret. He explained that when he was in the army going through the officer's training programme, all the students received severe demerits for cursing. To fill the need they had a meeting and invented an alternative curse that had no meaning but sounded blood-curdling.... "suckahatch". I still use it.

The Río Coco forms the border between Honduras and Nicaragua. Klee and Specht swam across to claim the latter for our group of modern conquistadors. Russ and I headed upstream. We had seen a feeder stream and lagoon from the air, but it turned out to be a lot further than we thought. We were delighted to accept a ride from an old fisherman with a good-sized dugout. This was by far the best collection we made "by air". We caught our only *Amphilophus margaritifer* (previously referred to as *A. longimanus*) there. We also found *Phallichthys amates* (the Merry Widow livebearer) which we had not previously seen in Honduras. In addition we found the fol-

Top, from left to right: Dr. Albert Klee, the author Ross Socolof, the late Russell Noris, and Dr. Harry Specht. Photos by Ross Socolof.

lowing other cichlids: *A. spilurus, N. managuensis, N. friedrichsthalii, A. robertsoni,* and *V. maculicauda.*

Our final landing was at a farm alongside the Río Aguan, about five kilometres from Durango which was not far from Trujillo on the coast. Again difficult collecting and nothing noteworthy caught.

This phase of the trip was over. We were all disappointed. We had learned that it was not practical to expect good collecting from landing "blind". The next day we expected great results. We would take the road from La Ceiba to Trujillo, clearly marked "route 5" on our maps. After going about twenty kilometres on a worse than terrible road it just ended; it had been washed out and was impassable. We learned

that the road (which Klee was now calling "route one half") had been this way for years. We had run out of road just as we were getting close to a town called Jutiapa which was the first and best looking of two isolated pockets we had seen on our map. But we could go no further and had to return to La Ceiba. We felt like a bunch of blind dogs in a meat house. We could smell it and couldn't find it. The only stop on the way back was when Klee and Specht drove off the road to buy bananas. Russ and I told them that they were plantains (cooking bananas), and not eating bananas. Klee and Specht insisted that they were bananas. They bought them and ate them. As a result they got smarter, along with

1. Río Bellaire in the dry season.
2. *Nandopsis motaguensis* from the Río Copan.
3. *Amphilophus margaritifer* from the Río Coco.
Photos by Rusty Wessel.

serious stomach cramps almost immediately.

We left La Ceiba after promising ourselves we would some day return and collect "route one half". We stopped to seine a few spots on the road back to San Pedro Sula. We had four boxes ready to ship. I had decided to send them to my Gulf Fish Hatchery in Florida rather than take them along on the balance of the trip. We got to the airport at San Pedro Sula after collecting some of the new spot-tailed mollies for Dr. Miller. We would spend our last three days at Copan after we had sent the fishes. Copan was another four hours north. Our plan was to visit the ruins and collect the area.

At the airport we ran into a brick wall. The fishes could be shipped but needed "proper" documentation. This included an inspection by an elusive phantom Honduran veterinarian to certify they were healthy. The flight we wanted to use left for Miami in four hours. We consumed three of these hours running around in circles. Suddenly light dawned. We collectively realized we were being held up for "mordida" (bribes). Not wanting to make the situation worse (I was still quite naive) we decided not to approach the cargo people directly — I was afraid we would insult someone. Instead I asked a young Honduran at the tourist desk to ask "the enemy" (cargo department) if we could speed things up for US$50.00. He came back smiling and said it was done and the fishes would be loaded as soon as they received the US$15.00 that I had promised. I saved $35.00 because of my terrible Spanish. I gave the saving to the magician from the tourist desk.

Copan is a wonder: it is the most interesting of all the Mayan ruins. The collecting in the area was excellent. We caught our first *Chuco microphthalmus* in the Río Amarillo about 5 kilometres west of Copan. This is a fish that deserves more attention as it is rare in the hobby. We also caught both *Thorichthys aureus* and *N. motaguensis* besides the other cichlids that had already been taken on this trip. Our stay in Copan was the most enjoyable part of the trip. Everyone enjoyed Honduras and its pleasant people. We all agreed that the fish fauna in Honduras could in no way equal the variety available in Belize.

Harry Specht and I continued to dream of trying to collect the road ("route one half") south of La Ceiba for almost twenty years. We were sure it held some fishes. In 1990 we were ready to give it another try. We felt certain that the United States Government had made an improved road south to Trujillo during the year or so that the U.S. Army was in Honduras during the Nicaraguan Contra rebellion. Rusty Wessel asked to join Harry Specht and myself on this trip and the three of us made the journey that spring. I had business in Belize and Rusty had a friend there in the Peace Corps whom he wanted to visit, so we all met at Russ Norris's house in Belize City. Russ could not go along this time as his health was failing — a sad note. The three of us flew into San Pedro Sula, our priority goal to try and reach the previously inaccessible area....

A collecting expedition to Honduras — part two

Rusty Wessel

Following that first trip to Honduras with Ross Socolof and Harry Specht in the Spring of 1990, I found my calling. This passion for collecting wild tropical fishes has subsequently led me to return to this area for an additional 10 trips (and counting) over the past 5 years. Although all of Honduras is exciting to me, central Honduras is simply the best.

Some of the best collecting in Honduras exists in the central part of the country. East of La Ceiba, the Cordillera Nombre de Dios mountain range is entangled in the beautiful rain forests of Central America. The streams which originate in this mountain network flow towards the Caribbean and provide excellent collecting areas. A mountain range this close to the sea is one of the phenomena of Central America. Fortunately it provides excellent habitats for a wide assortment of tropical fishes.

The Belleaire, Hauron, and Jutiapa rivers, which are part of the Papaloteca watershed, originate in the coastal mountain range near the town of Jutiapa. This area can be reached by taking a wonderful new road that runs between Trujillo and La Ceiba. This is Dr Klee's old "route one half" (now called CA 13). The water supply for these river systems comes from the clouds that constantly abut the highest peaks. These pristine mountain streams are among the purest and most beautiful rivers of Honduras. The

large boulders. In midstream the water can reach a depth of 2½-3 metres. The banks are lined by the lush green rain forest. Entangled vines cascade down from the canopy of trees and often touch the water's surface. The rivers team with life and provide a wonderful place to snorkel. It should be noted that these wonderful clear streams often become dangerous raging torrents during the height of the rainy season. The bridge on the Jutiapa river was completely washed away during the storms in 1993. The locals told me the water was 10 metres over the bridge. An incredible force of nature.

A most unusual and probably undescribed plant grows in the rapids of these mountain streams. This fernlike plant anchors itself to boulders submerged in the rapids. It grows only in the rapids and apparently prospers where the water flow is strongest. Because of its habitat, one can hypothesize that the species either has to have running water to survive or is eaten by fishes and/or other aquatic creatures if it attempts to grow in the calmer areas. Maybe someday someone will do some research on this exotic plant and give us some answers?

Other inhabitants of the streams include *Agonostomus monticola* (a mullet-like fish), *Rhamdia motaguensis* (a grey catfish), *Astyanax mexicana* (commonly called the Mexican Tetra), an undescribed *Poecilia*, and *Anguilla rostrata* (an eel). At least 4 types of goby exist in

1. *Ther*aps wesseli* exhibiting neutral colour pattern.
2. *Archocentrus spilurus* ("cutteri"); female with fry.
3. A pair of *Theraps wesseli* guarding their offspring.
Photos by Rusty Wessel.

water clarity during the dry season (January to June) is spectacular. The crystal-clear streams consist of fast-moving water with a current of approximately one metre per second, a pH of 7.5, and a water temperature of around 26° C (78° F). The bottom consists of sand, rocky rubble, and

the streams: *Gobiomorus dormitator*, *Eleotria pisonis*, *Awass banana*, and *Sicydium gymnogaster*. The *Sicydium* species is interesting because of its fused pelvic fins which are used as suckers, enabling the fishes to hold onto boulders in the fast-moving waters. Interestingly, these animals occupy the same territory as some of the cichlids of the streams. Freshwater crabs and large shrimps also

mal disappears into the gaps between the large boulders and wedges itself completely out of sight, making the capture of this elusive cichlid extremely difficult.

I vowed to return and catch live specimens. Eventually, after five different trips to this river spanning a two year period, I was fortunate enough to be able to collect wild adult specimens. The secret was the dark. Braving the rapids at night (with great difficulty), I was able to (hand)net adults sleeping on the bottom with the help of underwater diving lights. Approximately 25 nights of collecting resulted in 14 adult specimens, only 3 of which were male. This large disparity in the sexes seemed to exist in all three streams that I sampled. Thanks to the help of Dr Miller, the "Honduras Rapids Cichlid" has been officially described as *Theraps wesseli*, for which I am very thankful.

The adult *T. wesseli* looks somewhat similar to the Lake Malaŵi cichlid *Melanochromis auratus*. Even more interesting is the fact that during the breeding season the coloration of the females, and to a lesser extent that of the males, turns half black, similar to that of the male *M. auratus*. As far as the aquarium hobby is concerned, the greatest asset of this fish is the coloration, and hence probable popularity, of the juveniles. Most Central American cichlid fry are either dull brown or dull grey. At 3 cm this fish looks just like its parents. This fish has been bred in the United States (in Louisville) and the fry distributed, and should ultimately prove popular with hobbyists.

scurry about on the bottom in search of food.

Although all of the fishes in this Papaloteca watershed are enjoyable, it is the cichlids that are the most exciting. The slack areas are inhabited by *Amphilophus robertsoni*. This medium-size blue cichlid constantly sifts through the sand for food. It avoids fast-moving water and is quite at ease in the warmer backwaters. *Archocentrus spilurus* is well-represented throughout these streams, but seems most at home in moderately-flowing water, generally keeping to shallow areas. As with many cichlids, the taxonomy of this particular form is unclear, and the local colour morph of *A. spilurus* has in the past been assigned to a separate species, *A. cutteri*. Its correct nomenclature is still subject to debate. One thing is for sure, with the beautiful blue streak through the mid-section of the body and its wine-coloured fins, it is at the very least a quite distinct colour morph of *A. spilurus*.

Only one cichlid species lives in the fastest part of the rapids. The very first survey of this area gave rise to an astounding event: while snorkelling I saw a cichlid I had never seen before! I screamed for Ross to come and see it. He did and agreed it was a species he had never seen before either. We saw several other specimens, but were unable to catch a single one on the first trip. Sketches were made and sent to Dr Robert Miller, curator of fishes at the University of Michigan. We were positive we had seen an undescribed cichlid in the rapids. This in itself was surprising, especially considering the thorough survey performed in 1972 by Michael Martin, who spent 7 months in Honduras and preserved about 26,500 specimens from 182 localities including this drainage. However, after years of knowing this fish it is quite understandable why it was missed. This new cichlid gem is very agile in the rapids and quite rare in the river. Conservatively estimated, there is only one of these new cichlids to every 1,000 fishes in the stream. When approached or disturbed in any fashion, this ani-

Amphilophus nourissati, an interesting earth-eater from Central America

Michel Keijman

When talking of "earth-eaters", we are immediately reminded of the fishes of the genera *Satanoperca* and *Geophagus* from South America. These cichlids have a specialised feeding habit which consists of picking up a mouthful of substrate which is then chewed and filtered in search of anything edible. In Central America too we find cichlid species with similar feeding behaviour. They are currently grouped in the genus *Amphilophus*, and among them we find *A. citrinellus*, *A. alfari*, *A. lyonsi*, *A. macracanthus*, *A. rostratus*, and *A. robertsoni*. The following meristic and morphological characters must be present for a Central American cichlid species to belong to the genus *Amphilophus*: a pointed head with a long snout, a straight upper profile, long pectoral fins, and 5 to 9 bars on the body.

The description of Nourissat's earth-eater

In 1989 an article about the genus *Theraps* by Robert Allgayer was published by the French Cichlid Association (Association France-Cichlid): Révision et redescription du genre *Theraps*, Günther, 1862. Description de deux espèces nouvelles du Méxique (Pisces, Perciformes, Cichlidae). Allgayer explains his opinion regarding the delineation of the genus *Theraps*, and describes two new species, *Theraps belone* and *Theraps nourissati*, the latter named after the president of the French Cichlid Association, who has discovered many cichlids in several parts of the world. Allgayer also gives a diagnosis of the genus *Theraps*,

but at the same time states that his *T. nourissati* does not conform to the characters given! The body depth of *nourissati* is contained less than 2.5 times in the standard length, while all *Theraps* should have their body depth contained between 2.5 and 3.3 times in the standard length. Because the morphological characters of *nourissati* fit the diagnosis of the genus *Amphilophus*, I have herein assigned it to this genus.

Distribution

According to available information, the distribution of *Amphilophus nourissati* encompasses a number of tributaries of the Río Usumacinta, namely the Ríos Chancalá, Chocoljá, Corzo, and Lacanjá in Mexico and the Ríos Chixoy, de la Pasion, and Sayaxche in Guatemala. The Río Usumacinta forms, for a large part of its length, the border between Mexico and Guatemala. As far as I know *A. nourissati* has never been found in other river systems. An interesting observation is that *A. nourissati* has not yet been found together with another member of the genus *Amphilophus*, *A. robertsoni*, although the latter has an overlapping distribution and one would thus expect to find both species in the same river, at least in places. *A. robertsoni* and *A. nourissati* closely resemble each other.

The biotope

The feeding habits of *A. nourissati* predict that it will be found in the calm sections of rivers where the flow is minimal. Such places are usually found in small creeks, pools, and along the river banks. Because of the slow current, sediment can settle on the bottom, and this seems to be a prerequisite for the type of feeding substrate preferred by *A. nourissati*. I was able to observe a group of adult and sub-adult individuals feeding in the Río Chancalá. The substrate in that particular section consisted of leaf litter, sediment, sand, and other terrestrial material washed into the river. *A. nourissati* dive deep into the soft substrate, usually up to their eyes, and take a mouthful. During the ensuing chewing and filtering a lot of useless material is expelled via the gills. When all the edible material has been extracted the remaining substrate is spat out, and the entire ritual is then repeated.

Experience with this species in the aquarium has taught me that it has a very shy nature and can usually be found beneath branches or behind slabs leaning against the rear glass of the tank. In the rivers I found juvenile and sub-adult *nourissati* in large schools, not only in the previously mentioned calm areas, but also in the middle of the stream where the water sometimes flows very rapidly. The observation that juveniles of this species are commonly seen in schools suggests that it is advisable to keep young individuals in groups in the aquarium as well.

A. nourissati shares the habitat (dependent on location) with the following cichlid species: *Chuco intermedius, Herichthys pearsi, Nandopsis friedrichsthalii, N. salvini, Theraps irregularis, T. lentiginosus, Thorichthys helleri, T. meeki, T. pasionis, Vieja argentea*, and *V. heterospilus*. Other common fishes are *Astyanax fasciatus mexicanus*, several *Poecilia* species, *Xiphophorus helleri*, and *Rhamdia guatemalensis*.

A. nourissati in the aquarium

As mentioned earlier, it is advisable to keep this species in groups, in particular when the individuals are smaller than 15 cm. This was the reason I brought two dozen *nourissati* back to Holland from a trip to Mexico, and divided them into two groups, one of which I gave to an aquarist friend. The juveniles,

which were about one centimetre long, were placed in a large tank in which they could grow quickly. At a total length of about 7 cm, I noticed increasing aggression among the fishes, expressed as continuous chasing of one another. In the course of a year the fishes attained a total length of about 10-12 cm, but I was still unable to see any sexual differences. As the fishes continued to grow I placed them in a larger tank with a capacity of 1,000 litres.

The tank decor was as follows: the substrate consisted of a 7 cm thick layer of sand and fine gravel and many smaller stones and rocks. Large slabs were leaned against the back glass and along the sides, and bogwood was placed

Facing page: *Amphilophus robertsoni* from the Río Pichucalco near Santa Ana.
Right: The Río Corzo in Chiapas, Mexico.
Inset: *Amphilophus nourissati* caught in the Río Chancalá.
Photos by Michel Keijman.

minimum and only two GroLux tubes were used. The water was filtered through an external biological filter with a capacity of 75 litres and circulated by a pump with a capacity of 2,000 l/hr. In some parts of the tank the current was relatively strong, but in others there was hardly any water movement; these latter areas were preferred by *A. nourissati*.

During the following months I noticed that some individuals sometimes showed an unusual type of behaviour which consisted of two fishes facing each other, in a slanting, head-down position, the throat distended, and the entire body quivering. This ritual would last for several days, after which the protagonists changed colour pattern overnight. The normally brown ground colour became yellow, and 7 black vertical bars replaced the horizontal stripe which is the most prominent feature of the neutral colour pattern. The third and fourth bars broadened and fused in the middle and formed a black blotch on the centre of the body.

Only now could I see the difference between male and female. The male developed a steeper forehead and there was even a small nuchal hump visible. The otherwise barely visible black spot on the dorsal became prominent and the numerous blue iridescent spots on the body intensified. The black spot in the dorsal was prominent in the female as well, and two to three times as large as that of the male. The female, the

against these slabs. Tankmates were *Herichthys pearsi*, *Theraps lentiginosus*, and *Vieja argentea*, all species which are found together with *A. nourissati* in the wild. Because of the shyness of *A. nourissati* I kept the light above the tank to a

smaller of the two, also exhibits blue spots but these are not as numerous as in the male. In the meantime the genital papillae of both fishes became visible.

After these two fishes had changed colour they began defending a small territory with a diameter of about 40 cm at the lefthand front of the aquarium. They also started to clean a flat stone on the bottom and gradually removed the sand around it. Regarding their territorial defence, I would comment that they chased only smaller tankmates. I found that the pair "tolerated" the larger *V. argentea* and *H. pearsi* within their territory, even when they came close to the cleaned stone in the centre. After two days of cleaning and removal of sand, the genital papillae of both male and female were completely extended, indicating that spawning was at hand.

This was an exciting moment for me because *A. nourissati* had not yet been bred in the aquarium. At last these shy animals started to spawn. The first few runs did not produce eggs but then rows of 1.5 mm diameter, whitish eggs were laid on the stone, and immediately fertilized by the male be-

lized or not, but I could see some that were fungussed. This was an indication that not all the eggs were fertilized, which made my wait during the next few days all the more exciting. On the second day more eggs were white, but I could see that in the majority cell division had taken place. On the third day the fertilized eggs were almost fully developed and about to hatch. The larvae were chewed out of their eggshells by the female, who then moved them all to a small depression between some stones. Six days after spawning the fry were free-swimming and *A. nourissati* had been bred.

This first spawn contained about 80% unfertilized eggs, a high percentage which was repeated in later spawns. The cause of the inefficient fertilisation could not be determined. The pair, the male with a total length of about 18 cm and the female about 15 cm, spawned several times and each time the broods contained about 300 to 400 eggs.

1. Head profile of an adult male *Amphilophus nourissati* exhibiting a nuchal hump.
2. A pair *A. nourissati* preparing to spawn.
3. The female depositing eggs on a small stone.
Photos by Michel Keijman.

fore he chased away the *T. lentiginosus* that were eyeing the spawn. After about 30 minutes spawning was over and the female positioned herself over the eggs and fanned them. The male's task was mainly the defence of the territory.

Despite the presence of eggs, both male and female still allowed the larger tankmates into their territory. Fortunately these intruders had not seen the eggs, otherwise they would without doubt have been eaten. A day after the spawning I could not tell whether the eggs were ferti-

References

ALLGAYER, R. (1989) Révision et redescription du genre *Theraps* Günther, 1862. Description de deux espèces nouvelles du Mexique (Pisces, Perciformes, Cichlidae). *Rev. fr. Cichl.* (French Cichl. Ass.) 90: pp 4-30.

KEIJMAN, M.C.W (1992) *Cichlasoma nourissati* NVC Periodiek Nourissati 1-6 (Dutch Cichl. Ass.).

STAWIKOWSKI, R. & U. WERNER (1985) Die Buntbarsche der Neuen Welt (Mittelamerika) Edition Kernen, Germany.

The forgotten *Thorichthys maculipinnis*

Juan-Miguel Artigas-Azas

The Río Papaloapan or Río de las Mariposas (river of the butterflies) flows down from the volcanic highlands of the Mexican plateau, originating from cold water springs in these mountains. At first a rapid mountain stream, further downstream the river becomes wider and flows peacefully across a landscape characterized by tropical lowland vegetation, eventually emptying into the Gulf of Mexico at the city of Alvarado, between extremely beautiful salt lagoons. The drainage of the Papaloapan and its smaller tributaries is bordered to the north by a volcano belt 60 kilometres north of Veracruz, the state capital. This belt is the remains of a large volcanic chain which once extended from the central part of the country to the Gulf of Mexico, and meets the sea at Punta del Morro, just south of the 20th parallel north. This mountain chain acts as an effective geographical barrier to the spread of the freshwater fishes.

The taxonomic background of *Thorichthys ellioti*

In 1904 Seth Eugene Meek recognized an inhabitant of this basin as a new species which also justified the erection of a new cichlid genus, *Thorichthys*. The diagnosis of this new genus reads: "Body deep, much compressed; mouth rather small; caudal fin lunate, its outer rays produced into a filament; pectoral fin long and pointed, about as long or longer than head; subopercle with a black blotch, otherwise as in *Cichlasoma*". Additional traits were also mentioned, including a small size of no longer than 6 inches (about 15 cm), the absence of a nuchal hump, and a large variability between populations.

The name *Thorichthys*, Meek explains, stems from the Greek, and means "a fish that leaps", but gives no further explanation of his choice of name. Species listed by Meek as suitable for inclusion in his new genus were *Cichlasoma aureum*

(Günther), *C. affine* (Günther), *C. friedrichsthalii* (Heckel), *C. rostratum* (Gill & Bransford) and *C. longimanum* (Günther). Officially Meek recognized only two species: *Thorichthys helleri* (Steindachner) and the new *Thorichthys ellioti*, named after Professor D.G. Elliot, curator of the Zoology Department, Field Columbian Museum.

Thorichthys ellioti was described from material collected at Motzorongo, Veracruz (Lat.18°15' N., Long 96°43' W.), stored in the Field Columbian Museum (Field Columbian Museum, 4727). The publication also includes a drawing. Motzorongo, the type locality, is located on the Tonto river, one of the main affluents of the Papaloapan river system. Over the years extensive collections of this species have been carried out, which remain stored in museum collections around the world.

The genus *Thorichthys* was later designated a section of the genus *Cichlasoma* by Regan in 1905. Regan recognized three species in this

1. A male *Thorichthys maculipinnis* in the Río Otapa.
2. Río Dos Caños, a tributary of the Río San Juan Evangelista, near Hueyapan de Ocampo.
Photos by Juan-Miguel Artigas-Azas.

section: *C. aureum* (Günther, 1862), *C. affine* (Günther, 1862), and *C. callolepis* (Regan, 1904). *Thorichthys ellioti* was considered a junior synonym of *Cichlasoma* (*Thorichthys*) *aureum*, together with *C.* (*Thorichthys*) *helleri* (the second *Thorichthys* described by Meek) and *Heros maculipinnis*, a species described by Franz Steindachner in 1864. Later, in 1907, Meek considered *Thorichthys* a subgenus of *Cichlasoma*.

C. ellioti and *C. helleri* were again considered distinct species by Newton Miller (1907) and by Carl L. Hubbs (1936), an opinion which was later followed by Robert Rush Miller (1961), who also gave additional characters for differentiating the then *Cichlasoma* (*Thorichthys*) group. Kullander (1983), in restricting the genus *Cichlasoma* to its

South American representatives, left most Central American species without any formal generic placement, but regarded *Thorichthys* as a group "that should be recognised as a separate genus". Robert Rush Miller (in a recent posting (1996) on the Internet: Cichlid-L: the cichlid systematic and distribution Internet list) considers *Thorichthys* a valid, monophyletic genus with nine representatives (one yet to be described).

The neglected description

In 1864 Steindachner wrote a paper describing several now well-known Central American cichlids: *Heros lentiginosus, H. helleri, H. bifasciatus, H. gibbiceps,* and *H. maculipinnis.* The last of these matches in all taxonomic aspects the description of *Thorichthys ellioti* by Meek. Moreover the type locality of *maculipinnis* is given as Río Jamapa, which belongs to the Papaloapan river system, and from which *T. ellioti* was also described. The type localities of *T. ellioti* and of *T. maculipinnis* are not far from one another. Besides this taxonomic information, a personal knowledge of the area and the fish fauna leads me to conclude that we are talking here about the same fish: thus *T. ellioti* is a junior synonym of *T. maculipinnis.* The Río Jamapa, although in the drainage area of the Papaloapan, is not a direct affluent of the large river but empties direct into the Gulf of Mexico. This fact may possibly suggest the recognition of *T. ellioti* as a distinct species but, knowing the cichlids of the entire

Papaloapan system, I feel this is highly unlikely.

Meek (1904), when describing *Thorichthys ellioti*, didn't recognize *Heros maculipinnis* as a member of his genus *Thorichthys*; this was rectified later by Regan (1905), who included it in his *Thorichthys* section. It is not hard to imagine why this happened. It seems that the specimen described by Steindachner as *Heros maculipinnis* has badly damaged fins and thus lacks some of the diagnostic characters recognized by Meek for *Thorichthys*. If both descriptions are proved to refer to the same species, as I think likely, the name *maculipinnis* will have precedence over *ellioti*, which will then become a junior synonym of it.

Range

Thorichthys maculipinnis inhabits the entire lowlands of the Papaloapan system below an altitude of 300 metres. All rivers with an average water temperature above 24° C are home to this beautiful fish, including large, wide rivers such as the Papaloapan itself as well as very small affluent creeks no more than a metre wide and 10 cm deep. As mentioned by Meek, variation in colour pattern and morphological characters is apparent in different geographical areas. Individuals inhabiting the Río San Juan Evangelista and its tributaries (the eastern arm of the Papaloapan), exhibit an intense and distinctive yellow coloration on the ventral area, which, together with the otherwise orange coloration of the fish, makes it look especially beautiful. Fishes from the central part of the system, including those from the Tonto and Papaloapan, have an enhanced

blue coloration on the scales along the sides (eg in the Río Obispo), as well as a stepped head and a longer snout. Specimens from the western part — Río Blanco and separate rivers such as the Jamapa — instead exhibit more and brighter bluish-green dots on the cheeks and lower part of the flanks.

The area in which *Thorichthys maculipinnis* occurs extends from the Gulf of Mexico in the east to the Mexican plateau in the west, and from the volcanic mountain chain running west-east to Punta del Morro on the coast in the north to the watershed of the Coatzacoalcos river system in the south.

1. *Thorichthys maculipinnis* in the Río Dos Caños.
2. A fry-guarding pair of *T. maculipinnis* in the same river. In Spring breeding pairs are very common.
Photos by Juan-Miguel Artigas-Azas.

Environment

The habitat is characterized by not very clear or decidedly murky water, sometimes with zero visibility, in slow-flowing rivers and lagoons, which mostly have sandy bottoms and lots of cover in the form of driftwood. Because of the often murky water, light penetration is minimal and aquatic plants are not present in most of the range; overhanging vegetation is, however, common. The banks and river bottoms are normally covered with a layer of tree leaves. The rivers are commonly surrounded by tall forest trees whose roots normally extend into the water,

providing additional cover for the *Thorichthys*. The chemistry of the water includes a pH between 7.5 and 8.0 and a hardness of about 8 DH. The temperature normally ranges between 25° and 28° C.

Fishes of many families live together w[...].e *Thorichthys*, sharing the rich habitat. The cichlid family is represented by *Petenia splendida*, *Nandopsis urophthalmus*, *N. octofasciata*, *N. salvini*, *Paratheraps fenestratus*, and *Paraneetroplus nebuliferus*. Many other fishes are present: catfishes, livebearers, killifishes, mullets, characins, and gobies.

Biology

After many hours of underwater observation in clear water rivers, I can say that the main character of *T. maculipinnis* is that of a gregarious cichlid. Groups of adults and juveniles wander through the habitat, always in close contact with the bottom and looking at it. They stop from time to time and pick up small animals located in the substrate, using their long snouts to poke into the sediment. The mouthful is chewed and inedible material expelled via the gills. They don't seem to possess a strong pharyngeal mill, so prey needs to be soft — snails are probably not taken. It is not particularly surprising that specimens from the middle part of the Papaloapan river system have a more pronounced snout, given that they normally live over muddy, instead of sandy, bottoms, and thus need to penetrate deeper into the substrate to capture their prey. A similar adaptation can be seen in some species of the *Nandopsis labridens* group in the Panuco system. Those *N. labridens* and *N. pantosticta* which forage over soft bottoms have a more pronounced snout than their counterparts living in rivers with sandy substrates.

Breeding takes place mostly from February to May, when males pick small territories (no more than 50 cm in diameter), normally in the slow-flowing shallow water under or close to the cover of overhanging vegetation or driftwood. They defend these territories, which usually have a small rock at the centre, and court passing females by extending their fins, opening their gill covers, and assuming a 45° "headstand" position. Many females respond to this courtship, approaching the male, circling with him a couple of times and assuming the same head-down position — and then leave. Later one female returns, and thereafter stays with the male. *Thorichthys* normally form colonies of several adjacent pairs. Some *Thorichthys* species seem to favour leaves as spawning sites, but this is not generally the case in *T. maculipinnis*, although sometimes it does. Interactions between neighbouring pairs are commonly seen and provide a very interesting spectacle. They assume a threatening pose, facing each other with the gills open, making small, ritualized, runs forwards and backwards, sometimes accompanied by sudden outbursts of aggression during which the fishes simultaneously lock mouths — although no damage is ever done. The black blotches on the gill covers of *Thorichthys* species, a characteristic of the genus (but absent in one representative (*T. callolepis*)), enable them to appear much larger than they really are: the distended gills and gular pouches, together with the black blotches, give them the appearance of a large fish when seen from the front.

Spawning normally takes place early in the morning and the eggs are placed in tight-packed concentric circles on the chosen small rock or pebble. No more than two or three hundred small eggs will be laid, and these are defended aggressively by both male and female, no matter what the size of the threat. When the eggs hatch (two days under aquarium conditions at 28° C) the wrigglers are placed in a small pre-dug pit,

normally located at the base of the spawning site. The fry take several days (five under aquarium conditions) to consume their heavy yolk sacs before they start swimming. Free-swimming fry stay in tight packs, closely guarded by their parents. It is important to note that unlike some other cichlids, members of the genus *Thorichthys* form pairs that always stay close together looking after their progeny, and facing any threat. The male leads the family in circles around the breeding area, never going far from the original spawning site. During such "strolls" the fry keep constantly together beneath the female, picking at small organisms found on the bottom. During the night the fry huddle beneath both parents, who normally choose a small depression in which to rest. Fry protection and leading lasts until the fry feel secure enough to venture around the habitat on their own, usually when they have reached between one and two centimetres total length. Large groups of juveniles are normally found picking in the substrate close to the banks in very shallow water and among the vegetation fringing the stream. They stay there until they are large enough to join the adults in deeper water.

At the point when the fry abandon their parents' protection, the pair splits up and male and female go their own way. As is the case with other *Thorichthys* species, sudden non-expected rains during the breeding season may completely sweep away a pair's effort, resulting in their having to start the breeding process all over again.

Some guidelines for aquarium maintenance

Thorichthys maculipinnis can be kept and bred successfully under aquarium conditions. Good water quality is a must for ensuring healthy fishes, which otherwise easily succumb to internal and external bacterial infections. The pH and the hardness of the water are not critical but it should be free of ammonia and nitrite. Although

T. *maculipinnis* can be kept and bred in aquaria as small as 80 litres, I would definitely not advise quarters smaller than 300 litres. In large aquaria one can observe reasonably natural behaviour which is mostly absent in smaller tanks. I usually provide my cichlids with a sandy bottom in which they can pick. Driftwood and cover should also be provided, as well as some sort of "dither fish" to help them overcome their shyness. Large cichlid companions should be avoided in normal-sized aquaria (eg 300 litres), although in very large tanks they shouldn't be a problem.

Special care must be taken when feeding *Thorichthys*. Although they greedily accept any

fare, fatty products, eg beef heart or poultry, must be avoided, as they can cause digestive problems. Pairs with fry can be kept in a community tank without much problem. Fry can take *Artemia* nauplii as a first food, and one should take special care to keep the fry well fed, otherwise they will develop permanent deformities during growth.

Conclusions

I am glad to be able to report that, in spite of deforestation and heavy pollution of many of the rivers in which *Thorichthys maculipinnis* is (or was) found, the existence of this little gem is not directly threatened although this may change in the near future. Hopefully the massive habitat destruction taking place in Mexico will soon be halted and reversed, before all its fishes are in danger of extinction.

References

HUBBS, C. L. (1936) Fishes of the Yucatan peninsula. *Carnegie Inst. Washington*, 457:157-287, pls. 1-15.

KULLANDER, S.O. (1983) *A revision of the South American cichlid genus* Cichlasoma *(Teleostei: Cichlidae)*, Swedish Mus. Nat. Hist., Stockholm.

KULLANDER, S.O. (1986) *Cichlid fishes of the Amazon river drainage in Peru*. Swedish Mus. Nat. Hist., Stockholm.

MEEK, S. E. (1904) The freshwater fishes of Mexico north of the isthmus of Tehuantepec. *Field Columbian Museum*, Vol. V: 1-252.

MEEK, S. E. (1907) Synopsis of the fishes of the great lakes of Nicaragua. *Field Columbian Museum*, Publ. 121, Zool. services, 7 (4): 97-132.

MILLER, N. (1907) The fishes of the Motagua river, Guatemala. *Bull. Amer. Mus. Nat. Hist.* 1984(4): 933-940.

MILLER, R. R. & C.N. BERNARD (1961) Variations, life colors and ecology of *Cichlasoma callolepis*, a cichlid fish from southern Mexico, with a discussion of the *Thorichthys* species group. *Occ. pap. Mus. Zool. Univ. Michigan*, Nr. 622.

MILLER, R. R. & J. N. Taylor (1984) *Cichlasoma socolofi*, a new species of cichlid fish of the *Thorichthys* group from Northern Chiapas, Mexico. *Copeia* 1984(4): 933-940.

REGAN, C. T. (1905) A revision of the fishes of the American cichlid genus *Cichlosoma* and of the allied genera. *Ann. Mag. Nat. Hist. Ser.* 7(16): 60-77, 225-243, 432-445.

REGAN, C. T. (1906-1908) Pisces. Biologia Centrali Americani.

STEINDACHNER, F. (1864) Beiträge zur Kenntniss der Chromiden Mejico's und Central-Amerika's. *Denkschr. Akad. Wiss. Wien.*, 23(2): 57-74, pl. 1-5.

Other sources: CICHLID-L, The cichlid systematic and distribution Internet list, maintained by Sven Kullander at the Swedish Museum of Natural History. To subscribe send an e-mail to LISTSERV@FREESIDE.NRM.SE with the following message contained in the text "Subscribe CICHLID-L (Your name)". (leave out the quotation marks and parentheses).

SOUTH AMERICAN CICHLIDS

Variation in *Crenicichla regani*

Frank Warzel

What is *Crenicichla regani* Ploeg, 1989? In princi-
ple this question is easily answered. One has
only to fish along the banks of a small stream
near Porteira, a left-bank tributary of the central
reaches of the Rio Trombetas, to find a small
Crenicichla, females of which have pitch-black,
light-ringed, ocelli in the dorsal. This is the type
locality of *C. regani*, one of 8 recently described
dwarf pike cichlids, the largest of which rarely
attains more than 10 cm (total length) in the wild.
According to the data given by Ploeg (1989,1991),
however, this small cichlid is distributed across

almost half of the Amazon basin, that is, a total
area of some 3 million km². Several different
populations are already known in the aquarium
hobby, and can often be told apart at first glance.

Taxonomic history

The name *Crenicichla regani* Ploeg, 1989 suggests a newly discovered species, but this cichlid
has in fact been known to science for quite a long
time. An expedition led by J.D. Haseman collected the first specimens back in the summer of

1909, at Villa Bella and Bastos in the Rio Guaporé drainage. Haseman (1911) identified these fishes as *C. macrophthalma* Heckel, a species with a general resemblance to dwarf *Crenicichla*, but which grows very much larger. The true *C. macrophthalma* was also collected, and described anew by Haseman as *C. santaremensis*, now regarded as a synonym. In the same work a female *C. regani* from Santarém was assigned to *C. dorsocellata*, despite deviating from the type in several details. Two years later C. Tate Regan (from whom *C. regani* takes its name) revised the genus *Crenicichla* for a second time: Haseman's *C. dorsocellata* from Santarèm was reassigned to *C. notophthalmus*, a newly-described species from Manaus, while *C. macrophthalma sensu* Haseman was thought to be identical with *C. wallacii* from British Guiana, described by Regan in 1905. This confusion can probably be

1. A male *Crenicichla regani* from the Rio Trombetas exhibiting an aggressive colour pattern.
2. *C. regani* female with fry approximately 7 weeks old.
3. *C. regani*, 5-week old juvenile.
All photos by Frank Warzel.

Ecology

The dwarf *Crenicichla* species known to date can be divided into two categories on the basis of differing habitats and associated adaptations. The first group contains relatively slender-bodied species, while those which are specialised for fast-flowing rocky streams are laterally compressed and deep-bodied. Because the adaptations of these lithophilous (rock-loving) species have evolved independently of one another, ie in different river systems, this grouping is of purely ecological significance and has no bearing on the phylogenetic relationships of the various species. According to locality data, it would appear that *C. regani* is sometimes sympatric with rather

explained by the fact that Regan had not personally examined Haseman's material and had based his identifications simply on the published descriptions. But it does serve to demonstrate that several of the dwarf *Crenicichla* are very closely related to one another.

better swimmers such as *C. compressiceps* Ploeg, 1986, *C. heckeli* Ploeg, 1989, and *C. urosema* Kullander, 1990. It seems, however, to have a preference for calm inlets and small tributaries which offer plenty of shelter in the form of leaf litter and dead wood. Odd specimens have also been recorded among blocks of lava (lower Rio Arapiuns), in rocky residual pools along the Rio Tapajós (along with *C. urosema*), over pebbles and boulders (Rio das Mortes), and in the relatively calm back-eddies of rapids (Rio Curuá). In all these instances the water is generally very soft (less than 50 µS/cm), acid (pH less than 6), and usually clear but slightly tea-coloured. Temperature varies from one locality to the next, with an

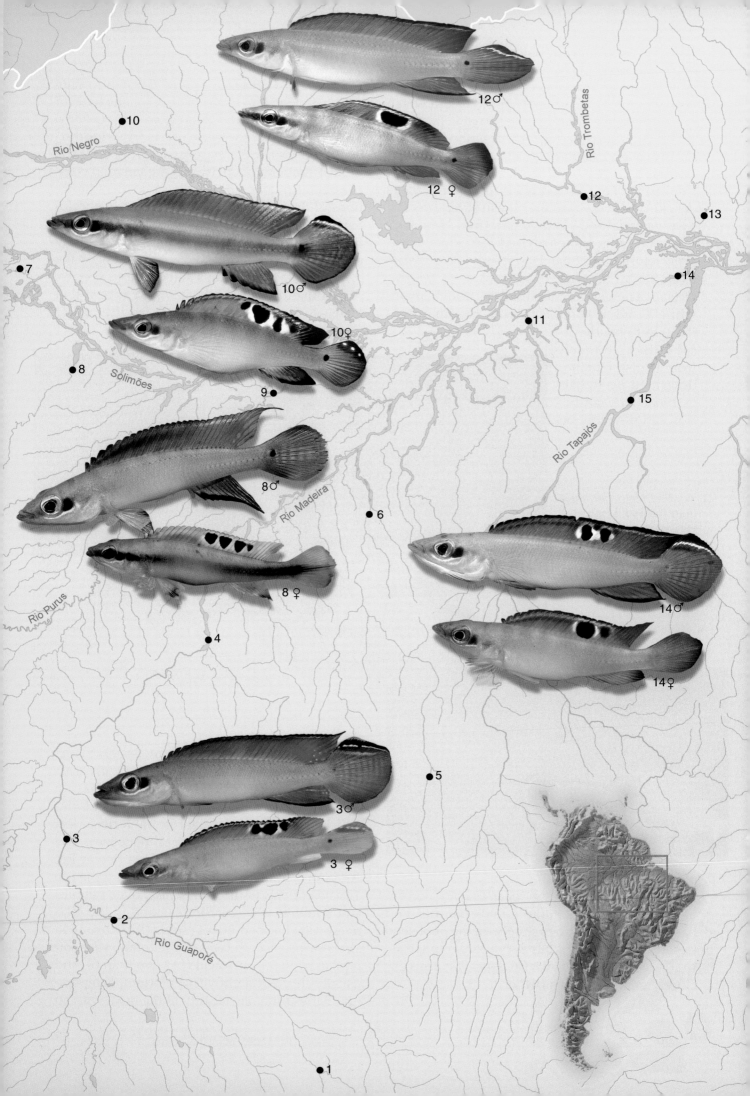

Rio Negro

Rio Trombetas

Solimões

Rio Madeira

Rio Tapajós

Rio Purus

Rio Guaporé

12♂

12 ♀

●10

●12

●13

●7

●14

10♂

●11

10♀

●8

9●

●15

8♂

●6

8 ♀

14♂

●4

14♀

●5

3♂

3 ♀

●3

●2

●1

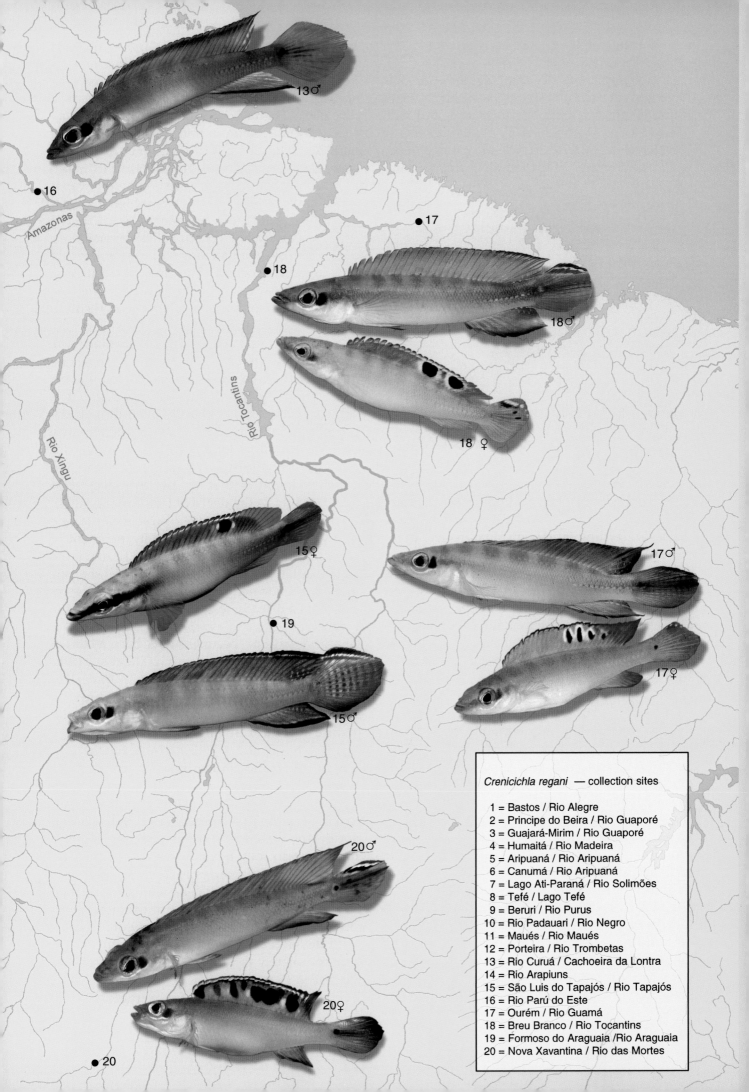

13♂

●16

Amazonas

●17

●18

18♂

18 ♀

Rio Tocantins

Rio Xingu

15♀

17♂

●19

17♀

15♂

20♂

20♀

●20

Crenicichla regani — collection sites

1 = Bastos / Rio Alegre
2 = Principe do Beira / Rio Guaporé
3 = Guajará-Mirim / Rio Guaporé
4 = Humaitá / Rio Madeira
5 = Aripuaná / Rio Aripuaná
6 = Canumá / Rio Aripuaná
7 = Lago Ati-Paraná / Rio Solimões
8 = Tefé / Lago Tefé
9 = Beruri / Rio Purus
10 = Rio Padauari / Rio Negro
11 = Maués / Rio Maués
12 = Porteira / Rio Trombetas
13 = Río Curuá / Cachoeira da Lontra
14 = Rio Arapiuns
15 = São Luis do Tapajós / Rio Tapajós
16 = Rio Parú do Este
17 = Ourém / Rio Guamá
18 = Breu Branco / Rio Tocantins
19 = Formoso do Araguaia /Rio Araguaia
20 = Nova Xavantina / Rio das Mortes

overall range of 22° C (Rio das Mortes) to 32° C (Tapajós residual pools).

The feeding habits of *C. regani* in the wild state have not yet been investigated. Goulding (1988) found small characins, *Apistogramma*, and killifishes in the stomach of *C. notophthalmus*, a closely related species. These prey items measured up to a third of the length of the predator

itself. Given that these two species are very similar in terms of dentition and body shape, it is reasonable to assume that *C. regani* is likewise a predator, feeding largely on small fishes. Compared to those of larger *Crenicichla*, the jaws are relatively short and less powerful, permitting the diet to be varied with other prey items, for example small crustaceans. Rheophilic species, above all *C. compressiceps*, are evidently more highly specialised towards this type of diet and appear to feed exclusively on invertebrates.

Reproductive behaviour

During the period from September to November the general area around Santarém was found to contain exclusively 6-month-old individuals which were either approaching sexual maturity or already ready to breed. From this we may conclude that these fishes spawn chiefly during the time of high water levels, when areas of the surrounding forest are inundated. Because it is very difficult to find these rather secretive dwarf cichlids in this habitat, we are obliged — as is so often the case with South American cichlids — to rely instead on aquarium observations.

As in all *Crenicichla*, courtship is initiated by the female. Curving her body in a U-shape and with fins spread, she displays in front of the male, who is at first completely indifferent, seek-

ing to win him as her mate. Failure is not at all uncommon at the first attempt. Only when the male in turn displays to the female, likewise with spread fins and U-shaped body, does pairing take place. Thereafter the pair perform a similar, recognition, display when, for example, they have been out of sight of each other for a short time. During this phase, in the course of which considerable aggression is shown towards tankmates, the newly-paired female seeks out a suitable spawning site; in the aquarium half coconut shells or clay pots, with as small an entrance as possible, are readily accepted. This need for security is very marked in many dwarf *Crenicichla*, and lack of suitable shelter may result in no eggs being laid.

The actual spawning may last for more than two hours, with male and female taking turns to enter the "cave". On one occasion the spawn — or rather a part of it — developed successfully even though the large male was unable to get into the cave. The fertilisation rate can, however, be adversely affected by a number of other parameters. It may be that low pH, as well as good water quality, is the decisive factor in the viability of the spawn. It is thus desirable to provide acid water conditions, because in the event of breeding failure the male is liable to drive the female out of her territory. In such cases the pair bond is not normally re-established until the female is again ready to spawn and begins to display.

Large aquarium specimens have been recorded as producing approximately 200 eggs, but in most cases the free-swimming fry number between 60 and 120 if the pH is maintained at around 6.0. The young are themselves sexually mature at about 7 months old.

Variations in colour pattern

The majority of *C. regani* females exhibit a pattern of several white-ringed ocelli on the posterior dorsal; these spots are often of varying size and may also sometimes intersect one another. This characteristic varies extraordinarily from individual to individual as well as from one population to the next, and, moreover, commonly changes as the fish grows. Older females often develop additional ocelli, or, conversely, may completely lack such spots, as is typically the case in *C. wallacii*.

Other dwarf *Crenicichlas*, for example *C. sp. cf.*

regani from the lower Rio Xingú (Warzel, 1992), *C. urosema* (Tapajós), and *C. heckeli* (Trombetas), exhibit white submarginal bands instead of ocelli, these bands visibly diminishing in brightness after the courtship phase. In *C. notophthalmus* from the Rio Negro, and in a closely related, as yet undescribed, species from the Orinoco system ("*C. wallacii*" in the aquarium literature), the ocelli are circular, normally free-standing, and sometimes ringed with red rather than exclusively with white.

It is more difficult to determine whether a variant from the Rio das Mortes belongs to *C. regani* or represents a distinct species. In this form, in contrast to the case in other dwarf *Crenicichlas*, the pattern of spots may extend forward to the anterior dorsal spines; moreover juveniles have only a very faint longitudinal band, although they exhibit many characters which are generally regarded as typical of *C. regani*.

Pointers to the identity of individual populations are to be found in the varying coloration of the dorsal fin in females. Most exhibit a bright red in the spinous portion (Tapajós, Tocantins, Trombetas), but there are also forms with light grey (Guamá), red-orange (Guaporé, Arapiuns), or orange (Negro), although the intensity of the colour depends on the status of the individual. Because males lack any striking pattern or coloration of this sort, it is rather more difficult to assign them to a particular locality, although they do sometimes exhibit characters which are apparently typical of a particular population.

It is, perhaps, interesting to note that individuals from relatively distantly separated localities can be very similar — as might instead be expected of neighbouring populations. *C. regani* females from the Rio Tapajós at São Luis, which have a red dorsal, resemble those from the distant Rio Tocantins more closely than those from the lower reaches of their home river. The latter, meanwhile, are very similar to those imported from the Guaporé. Morphological and meristic investigation of the various geographical varieties is needed in or-der to obtain a clearer picture of the situation. Perhaps such comparisons will also reveal zoogeographical links which no longer exist today. And answer, once and for all, the question of what is, and what isn't, *C. regani*.

References

GOULDING, M. , M. L. CARVALHO & E. G. FERREIRA (1988) *Rio Negro—Rich life in poor water*. The Hague, Netherlands: 200 pp.

HASEMAN, J. D. (1911) An annotated catalog of the cichlid fishes collected by the expedition of the Carnegie Museum to central South America, 1907-1910. *Ann. Carneg. Mus.*; 7: 329-379.

KULLANDER, S.O. (1990a) A new species of *Crenicichla* (Teleostei: Cichlidae) from the Rio Tapajos, Brazil, with comments on interrelationships of small crenicichline cichlids. *Ichthyol. Expl. Freshw.* 1(1): 85-93.

PLOEG, A. (1986) The cichlid genus *Crenicichla* from the Tocantins River, State of Pará, Brazil, with descriptions of four new species. *Beaufortia*;Vol. 36 (5); 57-80.

PLOEG, A. (1989) Zwei neue Arten der Gattung *Crenicichla* Heckel,1840 aus dem Amazonasbecken, Brasilien. *DATZ*; (42) 3: 163-166.

PLOEG, A. (1991) Revision of the South American cichlid genus *Crenicichla* HECKEL, 1840, with descriptions of fifteen new species and considerations on species groups, phylogeny and biogeography. Thesis, University of Amsterdam: 153pp.

REGAN, C. T. (1905) A revision of the fishes of the South-American Cichlid genera *Crenacara*, *Batrachops*, and *Crenicichla*. *Proc. zool. Soc. London* (1905): 152-168.

REGAN, C. T. (1913) A synopsis of the cichlid fishes of the genus *Crenicichla*. *Ann. Mag. Nat. Hist.* (8) 12: 281-283.

WARZEL, F. (1992) *Crenicichla sp. cf. regani*. *The Cichlids Yearbook*; Vol. 2: 82.

WERNER, U. (1991) Ein Zwerg, der riesig ankommt — *Crenicichla regani*, Ploeg,1989. *DATZ*; 44(10): 624-627.

1. *C. regani*, courting female from the Rio Negro showing the typical swimming behaviour.
2. *C. regani*, female from the Rio Cupari exhibiting a rare pattern: no spots in the dorsal.
Photos by Frank Warzel.

A new checkerboard cichlid from the Rio Tapajós

Frank Warzel

The members of the genus *Dicrossus* Agassiz, 1875, generally known in the literature as checkerboard cichlids, are among the most popular of South American cichlids. These darting, rather graceful, fishes are nowadays being imported more frequently, in particular on account of their interesting patterning, but also because of their splendid finnage. In addition they are very peaceful towards other aquarium occupants and thus appear well-suited to the community setup, but they are in fact basically rather delicate fishes, as becomes quickly apparent when an attempt is made to breed them — if not before. Thus, for example, *Dicrossus filamentosus*, which originates from a blackwater biotope, requires very acid water with minimal nitrate content. And aquarium decor which involves a bottom layer of scalded oak or beech leaves is not to everyone's taste. In their native waters these fishes are commonly found in quiet riparian bays or residual pools with an accumulation of leaf litter, dead twigs, and the like. Their typical method of searching for food — as in the rather larger *Crenicara* species as well — consists simply of grubbing around in the leaves lying on the bottom. An individual leaf is seized by its edge and the fish then swims upwards just far enough for the leaf to begin slowly to tip over; in this way it can turn over leaves that are much larger and heavier than itself. It would appear that these cichlids are searching for the small organisms that live beneath and among the layers of leaves, and which they pick up one at a time.

This behaviour is also exhibited by *Dicrossus* sp. "Tapajos", an undescribed species known only from a few specimens which were imported live to Germany in September 1992. This new *Dicrossus* is very easily distinguished from other members of the genus. While almost all members of the *Crenicara*-like genera, ie the checkerboard cichlids, have two rows of spots, *C.* sp. "Tapajos" has 3 longitudinal rows of black blotches. Another, again undescribed, species from the Rio Negro system exhibits a comparable pattern, but while in this latter species the individual spots are divided in the centre, those of *D.* sp. "Tapajos" are uninterrupted. Interestingly both the Rio Tapajos and the Rio Negro are each home to two *Dicrossus* species, one with 2, and another with 3, rows of spots. If we work on the assumption that relationships can be deduced from common colour patterns as well as morphological

1. As far as is known *Dicrossus* sp. "Tapajos" is found only upstream of the São Luis de Tapajós rapids.
2. A juvenile *D.* sp. "Tapajos" (TL ~25 mm).

3. An adult male *D.* sp. "Tapajos" (TL ~7.5 cm).
4. A male *D.* sp. "Rio Negro" from the upper Rio Negro system.
   Photos by Frank Warzel.
5. The distribution of the four known *Dicrossus* species .

● = *Dicrossus sp.* "Tapajos"
● = *Dicrossus sp.* "Rio Negro"
○ = *Dicrossus maculatus*
◐ = *Dicrossus filamentosus*
Localities according
to Kullander, 1990

features, then *D.* sp. "Rio Negro" and *D.* sp. "Tapajos" should be more closely related to each other than to the other *Dicrossus* species (with two rows of spots) found in the same river systems. A possible explanation for this would be that the "three-banded" *Dicrossus* are the geographically separated remnant populations of a species which was formerly far more widespread. It will probably come as no surprise to learn that both species are found in similar habitats, in both cases small streams with sandy bottoms, and rather acid (pH 5.5-6.5), relatively cool (24-26° C) water.

The specimens we observed, at 2-3 cm only half-grown, were seen singly over leaf-litter in shallow water near the banks. Larger individuals were rather rare. We likewise saw mainly juveniles of *D. maculatus*, which also originates from the Tapajós system. Their biotope contrasted with conditions at the localities in the upper Tapajós: crystal-clear lagoon-like areas of spring water, where the *D. maculatus* were generally found in the vicinity of stands of plants. In the Tapajós, as in the Rio Negro, the different species of *Dicrossus* appear not to be syntopic.

Breeding

Although it has so far proved impossible successfully to breed *D.* sp. "Tapajos", and thus establish it in the aquarium hobby, a number of observations on its breeding behaviour have been made. Like *D.* sp. "Rio Negro" (Windisch, 1992) and *D. maculatus* (Linke & Staeck, 1995) this species prefers to spawn in concealed sites. So although it was possible to observe the 30 minute-long spawning, the size of the clutch could not be ascertained. The female played the major role in the preceding courtship activity. The pelvic fins of the breeding female took on a reddish coloration and the two lowest rows of

6. A female *D.* sp. "Tapajos" in spawning dress (midlateral stripe pattern).
7. Female *D.* sp. "Tapajos" guarding 5-day old fry. Photos by Frank Warzel.

spots were replaced by a dark, slightly "washed out" band. After the pair had spawned — laying and fertilising alternately — the male showed no further interest in the eggs. This behaviour, rather atypical of substrate-spawners as a whole, appears to be the norm for the genus. As the eggs developed the male suffered increasingly frequent attacks by the female, so I removed him for his own safety.

At a pH of 5.2, a temperature of 26° C, and a conductivity of about 80 µS/cm (about 1 dH), it was on the 8th day after spawning that the female was first seen leading the fry around the tank, which was decorated with beech leaves, pieces of wood, and small bogwood roots. The small size of the fry at this stage was particularly striking. Unlike those of most other cichlid species, newly free-swimming *Dicrossus* fry are not yet capable of taking freshly-hatched *Artemia* nauplii, and as a result the original brood of 40, guarded attentively by the female, decreased in number day by day, even though the aquarium was well-established and should thus have contained adequate micro-organisms. And even though the surviving fry were able to take *Artemia* on the 4th day, it was not long before none were to be seen. It would thus appear that the conditions in the 70 litre aquarium were not optimal. Unfortunately no further breeding has occurred, so there has been no opportunity to experiment on the basis of what has been learned so far.

References

KULLANDER, S. O. (1978) A redescription of *Crenicara filamentosa* Ladiges, 1958 (Teleostei: Cichlidae). *Mitt. Hamb. Zool. Mus. Inst.*, 75: pp 267-278.
KULLANDER, S. O. (1990) *Mazarunia mazarunii* (Teleostei: Cichlidae), a new genus and species from Guyana, South America. *Ichthyol. Expl. Freshwaters*, Vol. 1 (1): pp 3-14.
LINKE, H. & W. STAECK (1992) *American Cichlids I: Dwarf Cichlids*. Tetra Press, Melle, Germany
WINDISCH, W. (1992) *Dicrossus spec.* "Rio Negro". *DATZ*, 45 (12): pp 767-770.

Mazarunia mazarunii — a rare South American cichlid

Willem Heijns

It is sometimes stated that all the cichlid species of South and Central America are known, and that new species are rarely found. By this is meant that although newly discovered or described species regularly appear, they are actually very similar to species already known; this in turn leads to debate as to whether the newly described species is in fact a distinct species at all. Examples of this are the recent descriptions of *Bujurquina* and some *Aequidens* species. Differences between some of these are discernable only by experts, and even they often need additional data, such as the collection site, to be sure. Nevertheless a sensational discovery is sometimes made, and one such being *Mazarunia mazarunii*.

The discovery of this species is not of recent date: the first two specimens, used for its formal description, were caught by Patrick de Rham in Guyana in 1976 (see his contribution in the next Yearbook, vol. 7). In 1982 it was determined by Kullander that these two specimens belonged to an as yet undescribed genus, but a formal

description was postponed as two small specimens were considered too small a sample. It would appear, however, that Kullander subsequently changed his mind on this point, as he subsequently (1990) described the species as *Mazarunia mazarunii* in an excellent leading article in the first issue of *Ichthyological Exploration of Freshwaters*.

In 1993 Frans Vermeulen, a well-known Dutch killifish expert, travelled through Guyana searching for new *Rivulus* species. He also collected a few specimens of *M. mazarunii* which he was able to take home alive. Unfortunately most of these died, but two individuals, a male and a female, survived and after some time ended up

A male *Mazarunia mazarunii* in the author's aquarium. Note the slightly bulging forehead. Photo by Willem Heijns

in one of my tanks.

Taxonomy and appearance

As mentioned earlier, the description of *M. mazarunii* is based on two specimens, which have a length of 5.34 cm (a male) and 4.75 cm (a female). The additional information given in this article is based on two other specimens, a male with a length of about 8 cm and a female of approximately 6 cm.

M. mazarunii resembles the species of the genera *Crenicara* and *Dicrossus*. The main characteristics in common are the structure of the first epibranchial bone (part of the first gill arch) and the snout profile. The main differences are the smooth edge of the pre-operculum and the shoulder girdle, and the presence of teeth on the fourth gill arch, both characters not found in *Crenicara* and *Dicrossus*.

The holotype of *M. mazarunii* is a young male. A photograph of it in the formal description shows an elliptical body shape and a slight frontal bulging of the head. The male in my tank is about two years old and has developed a nuchal hump, giving it a quite different shape. The structure of the mouth is unusual; in particular the lower lip has a peculiar shape, bulging left and right of the mouth giving it, when viewed from below, a hooked appearance. Moreover, because of this structure the mouth appears underslung. The unpaired fins are colourless and the rays are short. Kullander states that the dorsal and anal fins are rounded, but my specimens both have pointed fins, the male more than the female. Note, however, that the elongated ends of the fins and the female's tail are somewhat misshapen, probably caused by stunted growth (lack of proper food?). The normal shape of the tail is rounded. The colour pattern is not very spectacular, but is interesting enough to bear comparison with that of the checkerboard cichlids (*Crenicara* spp. and *Dicrossus* spp.). The characteristic colour pattern of these species consists of a number of dark, rather square, blotches arranged on a light background in a checkerboard pattern. In the formal description Kullander indicates that *M. mazarunii* is also a checkerboard cichlid. My two adult specimens, however, exhibit more or less complete vertical bars and a distinct horizontal stripe which is discontinuous in the male. The colour pattern of *M. mazarunii* is, as in many other cichlid species, dependent on the fish's mood. The above-mentioned pattern is exhibited when the fishes are in a neutral mood. When they get excited the pattern changes. In the female most of the bars

The female *Mazarunia mazarunii* exhibits different colour pattern depending on her mood. Both photos show the same female in different states of exitement: the upper photo shows the female in a neutral mood whereas it is seen excited in the lower. Photos by Willem Heijns.

disappear leaving a cross-like pattern consisting of the horizontal stripe and the central vertical bar. When the male is excited he loses all of his markings. The ground colour may also change when the fish is excited: the male retains his normal yellowish colour and exhibits a faint reticulated pattern but the ground colour of the female changes to more of a grey-blue. When the female is involved in courtship the pattern changes again: the horizontal stripe disappears and the middle bar intensifies, so that she somewhat resembles *Neetroplus nematopus*. The male shows a similar pattern when courting but his ground colour remains yellowish and he can thus easily be told apart from the female. Unfortunately the two fishes have not gone much further than courting, so that I cannot report on their breeding colours. In breeding *Crenicara* and *Dicrossus* it is the longitudinal stripe that is emphasised (see fig. 6 page 82). Another noticeable difference from species of those two genera is that the ventral fins of the female *M. mazarunii* are dark or black, instead of red.

Thus far the only known collection site for *M. mazarunii* is near the village of Kamarang in the extreme west of Guyana, where the Kamarang River flows into the Mazaruni River. Both the generic and specific names of this interesting cichlid derive from that of the latter river. Patrick de Rham and Frans Vermeulen both collected their specimens in this area, and up to now nobody has followed in their footsteps. The Peaima waterfalls further down the Mazaruni probably act as a barrier in the dispersal of *M. mazaruni*, which may therefore have a restricted distribution.

Kullander indicates that there is a close relationship between *Mazarunia*, *Crenicara*, and *Dicrossus*, claiming that *Mazarunia* is a sister genus of the other two. He calls these genera the Crenicarini. As mentioned earlier, the phylogenetic analysis of the formal description of *Mazarunia* is based on just two, small, specimens; with the presentation of two further, larger specimens these views may need to be reconsidered. The place of the Crenicarini among the South American cichlids is unclear. A relationship with the Geophagini has been suggested earlier (Kullander, 1986), as well as one with *Crenicichla*.

M. mazarunii in the aquarium

At the time of writing the pair have done little more than claim a site in the aquarium. They share their tank with six wild-caught *Cleithracara*

maronii and a pair of *Taeniacara candidi*. The aquarium is filled with rain water which is low in minerals (80 µS/cm) and has a slightly acid pH. As far as can be deduced from their behaviour, the two *M. mazarunii* are able to hold their own because the six keyhole cichlids are always in the open water while the *mazarunii* occupy the caves. *T. candidi* is so small that it generally escapes the attention of its tankmates. The *M. mazarunii* are, however, not yet prepared to do what everyone wants them to do, and are not as yet defending a specific site in the tank. Courting is regularly seen, and it is the female who tries to attract the attention of her partner. Exhibiting her "*Neetroplus*" colour pattern, she swims around the male who, unfortunately, does not react. Sometimes the male too adopts courtship dress, but quickly loses interest. Some digging activity has been noticed on rare occasions. The technique employed is unusual. Digging cichlids usually swim forwards out of the pit with a mouthful of sand, but *M. mazarunii* do it in reverse: they pick up small amounts of sand and almost always swim backwards out of the pit, even when they could have swum forwards.

All in all *M. mazarunii* is truly a completely new addition to our hobby, although we know very little about this species, scientifically as well as aquaristically. Moreover the extremely small number of specimens in captivity is unlikely to do much to alleviate this situation, so it is to be hoped that more will be collected in the near future.

References

KULLANDER, S.O. (1986). *Cichlid fishes of the Amazon drainage of Peru*. Swed. Mus. Nat. Hist. Stockholm, Sweden.
KULLANDER, S.O. (1990) *Mazarunia mazarunii* (Teleostei: Cichlidae), a new genus and species from Guyana, South America. *Ichth. Expl. Freshw.* Vol. 1 (1): 3-14.

A review of the current exporting operations from the African Rift Lakes

Stuart M. Grant

The African Rift Lakes. What a fascinating and image-evoking subject! Most of us have a broad knowledge of the area of Africa that encompasses these vast inland seas, and from our history lessons in school recall the sagas of their discovery by early visitors, mainly from Europe but also from the Arabian countries in the Middle East. Names such as Burton and Speke, Stanley and Livingstone, come to mind: redolent of history; of achievement; of privations, of heroism, of bravery, and sometimes regrettably less high moral values. Following later in the footsteps of these spectacular figures came other visitors — naturalists, botanists — and the era of the great collectors of natural material began, with specimens finding their way back to the universities and museums of Europe and the United States.

It is perhaps strange that although collections of fishes from the African lakes date back to the last century (eg Moore), and further major collections took place in the twenties (eg Christy), and in the thirties and forties, the concept of these fishes as desirable aquarium specimens really only developed with the advent of air travel and, of course, the jet airliner, which made the transportation of such fishes a feasible and practical proposition.

Over the past three decades collectors various have operated in and around these Rift Lakes. Some have passed naturally into history; some left voluntarily or involuntarily, having found that their interest/dream/obsession (call it what you will) was not practical or a realistic proposition. Some have, over a sustained period of years, begun to establish substantial collecting/breeding stations, usually adjacent or near to the source of their material. True, such facilities are not on a scale comparable with the giant ornamental fish complexes in Florida, United States, or Israel, or with the large Southeast Asian facilities occupying vast tracts of land, but progress — substantial progress — has been and is being made.

1

The significance of ornamental fish exporters and their activities in the riparian countries

In the case of Malaŵi, the ornamental fish export operation currently gainfully employs some 100 workers plus. A non-scientific study conducted to estimate the number of persons being 100% maintained or supported by the workers in question indicates that a factor of 1:10 is not far from reality. And when peripheral family and extended family members are included — on a periodic but nevertheless regular basis — a further five persons can be added to the commitment factor. This indicates that it is quite con-

1. Two divers putting their catch into the drum which is used to decompress the fishes.
2. The small compressor in the boat supplies pressurised air into two 50-metre long hoses.

ceivable that 1,000 persons derive virtually all of their livelihood from this enterprise and that a further 500 receive part-time assistance from their employed relatives.

Quite apart from the employment aspect, however — without which many workers would migrate to the already overcrowded towns and cities — the non-destructive aspect of the ornamental fishing activity needs to be emphasised. A wide and reasonably comprehensive coverage of the Malaŵi portion of the lake is being achieved with six open boats and 24 divers; compare these figures with the country-wide estimates of 12,000 fishing craft and over 40,000 traditional fishermen. And on the subject of food fishing operations, it must be mentioned that articles in the Malaŵi press have drawn attention to the serious situation regarding the depletion of fish stocks that has been and is taking place. Furthermore, and regrettable from the ornamental fish point of view, there is ever-increasing pressure with intensive seine netting operations "clearing" sandy beaches and,

in addition, moving closer and closer to rocky portions of the lake previously ignored. Some fishes from these areas that were formerly available for the ornamental trade are declining in numbers and becoming real rarities. And even within the National Park confines fishing for food fishes and rock-dwelling varieties is taking place on a regular basis. It should be mentioned that the authorities do what they can to reduce and prevent the use of incorrect fishing techniques, but the regulatory officials are thinly spread over a vast fishing area....

This "clearing" of certain fishes by local food fishermen is not just hyperbole — a paper prepared by researchers has demonstrated that in one portion of the lake there has been a 96% decline in the population density of shallow water molluscivorous fishes from 1978 to 1994. No ornamental fish collection takes place in this area.

In complete contrast, the ornamental fishing operations are selective and precise, with specified catch numbers being the rule, and welcome foreign exchange is received following shipment overseas. In the absence of a multi-exporter/exporting scenario — which can lead to a destructively competitive "catch 'em all quickly" philosophy — there is no incentive to "hammer" any particular species. Furthermore, as and when the range of fishes exported is progressively widened, the take-off becomes more and more spread across the various populations — thus easing the situation.

The non-destructive aspect of non-pressurised collection of ornamental fishes does need to be emphasised. Operations in Malaŵi have been conducted for more than twenty years, even longer at some sites, but there is no fish that was available years ago (using standard ornamental fishing techniques) that is not available at the present time.

Fishing techniques

In Malaŵi the "hookah" system of dive gear is used. It is basically a small petrol engine driving an oil-free low pressure compressor fitted in the dive boat. Through a reserve tank air hoses fifty metres long extend to a harness on the diver's back and chest. A standard second stage SCUBA regulator with mouthpiece is used. In essence it is similar to SCUBA diving but with air supplied from the surface as opposed to an aqualung cylinder. A boat team consists of four divers — two diving together at one time — and the divers change places as and when they get cold or tired. A lot of fishes are caught in depths of less than ten metres and the "hookah" arrangement is preferred to aqualungs, which require heavy and costly high-pressure compressors to refill. In other countries — Tanzania, Zambia, Zaïre — the aqualung system is generally used, but the "hookah" system is known and sometimes used as well. Generally, in Malaŵi, fishing and diving do not take place deeper than twenty-five metres — for safety reasons this is not encouraged — but in Lake Tanganyika diving can take place to depths way beyond this limit in order to secure the deep-water species that are sought after in the trade.

Nets in Malaŵi are essentially nine mm nylon mesh. A typical dive net is ten metres long and two metres deep when set. Weights ensure that the net sinks rapidly over the rocky substrate and it is draped by the divers over the rocks. In general fishes are guided into the net where they are caught by hand. The fishes are placed in holding drums with small mesh netting over the orifice, and when the catch is complete the drums are moved to the surface in stages. Decompression (an essential requirement for cichlids caught at a depth of seven metres or more) can take up to two days. Some fishes can be supplied to headquarters by catching boat; some are brought in from further afield using a larger diesel collection vessel; some, from distant collecting stations, are bagged with oxygen and sent down on one of the large lake vessels operated by Malaŵi Railways. This procedure enables fishes from a host of collecting points in the north to be brought into headquarters on a weekly basis. Emphasis should be placed on the fact that very specific catching requests are given, ie excessive numbers are not required.

Some fishes are caught by angling, some are caught by the use of traps, and a small percentage are obtained by direct purchase from local fishermen who have learned which varieties may be required for the ornamental trade. These are local arrangements close to the main holding centre which is on the lake shore.

In essence, catching operations elsewhere in the other Rift Lakes are similar but, as mentioned, aqualungs are used, with divers proceeding to considerable depths; and there does not seem to be an equivalent facility in other countries to the Malaŵi Railways collection vessel. This necessitates individual means of transportation of fishes over really substantial distances (at considerable expense) back to the respective holding centres.

The ideal of a composite fish facility (handling wild-caught and captive-bred material) is attractive, but the setting up of such an organisation is an expensive investment. Loans are virtually out of the question (chronically high interest rates usually prevail) and inevitably construction has to be financed out of profit and turnover. Nevertheless such facilities are developing and have been developed — perhaps not as fast as would be ideal — but the financial constraints in most

African countries are real and tangible. Carrying this trend to its logical conclusion it is possible, if not likely, that in the future the authorities will give preference to those exporters who have extended the spectrum of their operations to include a captive breeding component, with any exclusively wild-caught operators being encouraged to make the change.

Current exporting operations from the African Lakes

Lake Malaŵi

Stuart M. Grant (Salima, Malaŵi). Has operated since January 1973. Catching territory embraces virtually all of the lake in Malaŵi waters apart from National Park areas and the Tanzania coastline. Operations in Mozambique started in 1994 and it is intended to extend these as and when practical. Mozambique still refers to the lake as Lago Nyasa, its old name. Fishes are shipped out of Lilongwe International Airport to destinations in Japan, Europe, and the United States. The number of employees currently lies at around 100 persons. A large breeding house is under construction and an area has been demarcated for the introduction of ponds (covered with plastic tunnels), thus expanding the captive breeding operations.

Pomonda Fisheries (Mal-Ta-Vi, Hohenahr-Erda, Germany). The joint owner of this company operates out of Liuli in Tanzania with fishes being flown to Dar es Salaam airport by light aircraft (which can be a life-threatening undertaking; see photograph on page 90). A reasonably substantial holding centre has been established on the lake shore; operations are restricted to Tanzania territorial waters. Virtually all fishes are shipped into Frankfurt initially. Wild caught operations only.

African Divers (Dar es Salaam, Tanzania). This company is joint-owned by Swedish nationals who operate both on Lake Malaŵi within Tanzanian waters and also on Lake Tanganyika south of Kigoma and north of Kipili. It is believed that most fishes go to Stockholm, initially. Wild caught operation exclusively.

Lake Tanganyika

Rift Valley Tropicals (Toby Veall, Lusaka, Zambia). This company is operated by a British national based in Lusaka. Large permanent holding tanks have been built at the lake, near

1. A diver, using SCUBA gear, collects fish in Lake Tanganyika.
2. A section of the breeding compound of the author's establishment in Malaŵi.
3. Fishes are acclimatised for shipment in the fish-house at Kambiri Point, Malaŵi.
4. The fish-house of Pomonda Fisheries at Liuli, Tanzania. Photo by Annette Bentler.

Mpulungu, and a further batch of tanks at Kasanga, Tanzania, to the north. Operations take place along the Zambian coastline and also in southern Tanzania. "Deep water" operations in this area of the lake can be hazardous when sudden storms arise. Fishes are shipped to various clients in Europe and the USA. Substantial investment has been implemented by this organisation and breeding is being conducted on a modest scale. An increase in captive breeding is intended and planned. One European diver is employed in addition to some 60 African staff. Packed shipments are now brought by light aircraft from the lake (over 1000 kilometres away) to Lusaka International Airport for onwards despatch. The logistics of this exporting company are remarkable and a small emergency facility is maintained a few kilometres from Lusaka airport. Difficulties are being encountered with government fish levies being on a "per fish" base rather than "per box" — this penalises breeding operations and it is hoped that this aspect can be changed. Limited but welcome "breaks" in investment and purchases by the authorities exist on paper but tend to be lengthy in actual implementation. The owner estimates that 75% of the Zambian coastline has been covered during diving/collecting activities to date, by way of exploration. The tourist dimension is being followed up by this exporter — to diversify operations — and labour intensive practices are followed to improve the lot of local citizens. Estimated ratio of catching activities between the two countries: 25% Tanzania vs. 75% Zambia.

1. A section of the breeding/holding area of Lake Valley Tropicals near Mpulungu in Zambia.
2. The hand-made jetty protects the boats against bad weather on Lake Tanganyika.
3. Marc Danhieux barely survived a crash with the chartered aeroplane while transporting cichlids from Liuli to Dar es Salaam. Photo by Winter.
4. In the white basins fishes are acclimatised for shipment in the "fish-house" of Fishes of Burundi at Bujumbura.
5. Cichlids are bred in Burundi in outdoor ponds.

being delivered by light aircraft to Lusaka airport for onward transmission. Logistics are substantial —as for Rift Valley Tropicals. A limited number of clients. Wild caught operations only.

Aquaproducts (Kigoma, Tanzania). Tanzanian citizens of Asian origin who operate a hotel and water transport facilities for tourists wishing to cross the lake to the opposite coast. Has been in operation for a number of years, but shipments can be limited due to other work commitments. Fishes are shipped out of Dar es Salaam and transport by air — sector Kigoma to Dar es Salaam — can be difficult. Some shipments have been shipped by bus to Bujumbura, Burundi and on via the international airport there. Various customers but infrequent shipments. Wild caught operations only.

Fishes of Burundi (Bujumbura, Burundi). This is a major and impressive organisation that been functioning for well over twenty-five years. The founder of this company was the legendary Pierre Brichard, a Belgian who was well known and formally established in Zaïre, exporting riverine fishes from the Congo river complex. The daughter of Pierre Brichard and her husband now operate this large facility situated a few kilometres from the lake in Bujumbura. No

Blignaut Exports (Jeanne and Chris Blignaut, Mpulungu, Zambia). This is a sporadic exporter whose primary occupation is working with really large fishing boats on Lake Tanganyika, dealing with food fishes. An experienced exporter who ships periodically, with packed boxes

visitor can fail to be impressed at the care and dedication with which this export station is run, with some nine local workers at the holding centre. Burundi has only some 70 kilometres of lake shore so their access to wild-caught material is restricted, but wild catching operations using a number of Burundi skin divers and aqualungs (used by the two owners) take place. The owners being aware of the limitations imposed by the restricted access to wild material, over the years an outstanding array of breeding stock has been assembled from different parts of the lake and formidable numbers of quality bred fishes are produced, with particular emphasis on *Tropheus* species. The packing of consignments by this company is also legendary — for quality and reliability it is almost an industry standard. As this paper is being prepared a tense and worrying political situation exists in Burundi and it is hoped that a Rwanda type débâcle will never be allowed to happen. Breeding operations exceed wild-caught exports in numbers of fishes exported. This is indeed an operation unique in the Rift Lake scenario.

C. J. Aquarium (Hüllhorst, Germany). The owners of this company are actually Zaïre nationals with a large holding centre at Uvira. This exporting company extends its operations down the entire lake coastline of Zaïre — in extreme cases plus or minus six hundred kilometres! The main German client (C. J. Aquarium) has a large say in the direction of operations, and its owner regularly commutes from Germany to Burundi and drives across the border into Zaïre each day to oversee activities. Consignments are shipped out of Bujumbura airport in Burundi to various clients in Europe. A staff of some forty workers is engaged, including sixteen to twenty divers. Operations can be hampered by regular "outages" of electricity at the holding centre — frequently there are only some eight to ten hours of electricity per day/night. Essentially a wild caught operation, but a very extended one by virtue of the huge distances involved in collection.

Lake Victoria

Uganda Aquatics (Kampala, Uganda). This organisation is run under the umbrella of a non-government organisation with two British nationals directing operations. Interestingly, although some catching takes place from Lake Victoria itself, the main effort is currently being directed at other fishing locations in areas north of Lake Victoria, ie rivers, streams, and other,

smaller lakes. Although a small operation at the present time, success has been achieved; this portion of Uganda has interesting material that needs to be investigated and exploited. Brief residential instruction courses have been held at the Kampala holding centre to inform villagers from appropriate areas of what is required. They then catch and retain live fishes in their home districts in simple mud holding ponds (dug by them for this purpose) awaiting collection and delivery from headquarters in Kampala, and receive payment for same on the spot. By the nature of the enterprise only a small staff of some nine persons works at the headquarters. A key figure is the driver/collector who needs a good knowledge of the fishes he picks up on his extensive overland trips over appallingly bad roads.

Footnote

The information supplied above has been gathered from various sources and every endeavour has been made to ensure the correctness of information therein. There are also a number of other, smaller, operators/exporters, usually operating out of Lake Tanganyika: some come and go and some can be classed as "hit and run" operators who I believe will make no lasting contribution to the economy of the country where they operate. However, if any statement is incorrect or inaccurate I unreservedly apologise for this. S.M.G.

The age of cichlid fishes

Martin Geerts

At the turn of the century the well-known British explorer J.E.S. Moore (1903) surprised his fellow biologists by telling them that the cichlid fishes must have already been in existence in Jurassic times. As a matter of fact Moore had no direct evidence to support his views. Basing his conclusions mainly on the external characters of snails, he had formed the opinion that Lake Tanganyika had once been part of a sea that formerly covered all of the Congo (=Zaïre) Basin. When the sea withdrew from the continent (according to Moore's views, in Jurassic times) sea water remained in the deep trough that is nowadays filled by Lake Tanganyika. The sea water that remained subsequently slowly lost its salt content and the marine ancestors of the cichlid fishes managed to adapt themselves to the new lacustrine environment. And so Lake Tanganyika became the birthplace of the family Cichlidae, and from here representatives of that family colonised all of Africa as well as South America, Madagascar, and India.

Obviously it was difficult for Moore's contemporaries to believe that cichlids, i.e. modern perciform fishes, were once part of a prehistoric fauna which was dominated by dinosaurs and, insofar as aquatic environments were concerned, by ichthyosaurs. Apparently it was also very hard to believe that there once were "cichlidophageous pterosaurs". Moore's theories were laid to rest and a Jurassic origin for the cichlid fishes was not taken into consideration for a very long time. However, during the last few decades it has become clear that, in this, as in other respects, the world is continuously changing.

Many recent authors believe that the cichlid fishes should be placed among a prehistoric fauna and some authors go back far into Mesozoic times to place the origin of the cichlid fishes. For instance, the late Humphry Greenwood (1995) wrote most recently that the Cichlidae must have evolved during the Late Jurassic and the Cretaceous (from 146 to 80 million years ago). Even though it is not very likely that their development took some 80 million years, Greenwood's ideas support the views of Paul Loiselle (1995). According to the latter author no genetic engineering would be needed to accommodate the dinosaurs of Michael Crighton's *Jurassic Park* with a contemporaneous fish fauna. The cichlids of Madagascar would be perfectly suitable for that role. In fact Loiselle went even further when he stated that the distribution pattern of the etropline cichlids eloquently demonstrates that these fishes have to be more than 165 million years old. Another author, and one of Loiselle's sources, Lynne Parenti (1981: 534), came to the same conclusion. However, Loiselle apparently overlooked a statement by Briggs (1984: 19) who made short work of that idea, simply by pointing out that Parenti had placed both the cichlids and the killifishes in a pre-teleostean fauna! Rather like saying that the hominids are older than the mammals!

The fossil record

The fossil record of teleostean fishes was recently reviewed by Colin Patterson (1993a), who found that *Macfadyena dabanensis* is the oldest fossil Old World cichlid. In this he follows Van Couvering (1982), who states that this fossil fish is "questionably Oligocene". Another fossil cichlid, tentatively placed in the genus *Astatotilapia* by Micklich & Roscher (1990), is certainly of Oligocene date (32 - 27 million years ago). According to Patterson (*op. cit.*) the oldest fossil cichlids of the New World are *Aequidens saltensis* — treated as a geophagine cichlid in the writings of both Kullander (1983) and Casciotta & Arratia (1993) — and *Acaronia longirostrum* (recently redescribed by Casciotta & Arratia (*op. cit.*) as *Paleocichla longirostrum*). These cichlids, according to Patterson, are from the uppermost Oligocene or the Lower Miocene. In a recent paper Silva Santos & Santos (1993) give a redescription of a fossil cichlid they call *Tremembichthys pauloensis*. These authors feel that their specimen may be of Deseadean age. Berggren & Prothero (1992) state that recent dating has placed the Deseadean in the late Oligocene (28 - 21 million years ago).

Some authors still feel that the fossil fish described by Arthur Smith Woodward (1939) as *Macracara prisca* is as old as the Eocene, chiefly because Woodward himself believed so. However, more recently Stawikowski (1993) has placed this fossil in the recent genus *Retroculus*, while according to Maisey (1993) it is only slightly older than the fossil species mentioned earlier.

It is thus obvious that the fossil record most certainly does not concur with a hypothetical pre-Tertiary origin for the cichlid fishes, and such an origin becomes even more unlikely when we consider Patterson's remark (1993b: 48) about the fossil record of the perciform fishes: "No unquestionable perciform is yet recorded by Cretaceous skeletal remains". And the Cichlidae are generally thought to be members of the sub-order Labroidei, part of the order Perciformes, even though that classification is questioned by some authors (see Johnson, 1993). It is therefore most unlikely that the perciform radiation took place during the pre-Tertiary era.

The distribution of cichlid fishes

Of course some other authors have realised earlier that the fossil record does not support a Mesozoic origin for the cichlid fishes. For instance, Gray (1988: 131) wrote that the earliest Cichlidae appear in the Oligocene or possibly Eocene. But he then added the following statement: "... Their Gondwanan distribution and the fact that the earliest are 'fully cichlid', suggest that their evolution took place before the mid-Cretaceous 'break-up of the South American-African-Malagasy-Indian portion of Gondwanaland' which provides a better datum for their radiation in inland waters despite the absence of any positive pre-Oligocene fossil records". Indeed the proponents of a strict vicariance model feel strongly inclined to push the origin

of the cichlids far back in history. As is widely known, representatives of the family Cichlidae can be found in Africa (whence they entered the Levant), South America (whence they possibly migrated to Central America), Madagascar, and India. These regions once formed Western Gondwanaland, and apparently many biologists feel that cichlids were already in existence before the break-up of this supercontinent. With regard to the cichlid fishes, such biologists do not believe in dispersal. And so, according to Melanie Stiassny (1991: 3): "The Cichlidae probably arose sometime early in the Cretaceous, and taxonomic differentiation was well

A pterosaur with prey: *Paratilapia polleni* from Madagascar. Are cichlids old enough to have been the contemporaries of fishing pterosaurs?

under way prior to the separation of the Gondwanan fragments". Recently, however, the same author (Stiassny & Raminosoa, 1994: 143) has changed her mind drastically and now no longer believes in a strict vicariance model, feeling that the presence of the cichlids on Madagascar is probably best understood in terms of some type of post-rift dispersal. This simply means that the cichlid fishes arose somewhere else and later migrated to the "Grande Île" (Madagascar).

Cichlid fishes as a monophyletic assemblage

As we have seen, Stiassny (1994) now believes that the cichlids of Madagascar dispersed to the Grande Île during post-rift times. If cichlid fishes form a monophyletic assemblage (ie are descended from a common ancestor), and their present distribution is not the result of vicariance (the separate occurrence of corresponding species divided by a natural barrier), then their existence on all of the western Gondwanan fragments has to be the result of dispersal from some centre of origin. Stiassny (1981, 1993) does in fact believe

Ptychochromis oligacanthus, a Madagascan cichlid, is regarded as one of the oldest and most primitive cichlids known to date, but it is most unlikely that the cichlids originated *before* Madagascar became separated from Africa. So how did they get there?

that the cichlid fishes form a monophyletic assemblage. In her paper of 1993 she adduces three characters to confirm her view: the jaw musculature, the otoliths, and the intestine (which always exits the pouch-like stomach from the left, while the first intestinal loop always lies on the left side of the fish). However, the use of such characters is not without risk, as evidenced by the case of Pieter Gaemers (1989). This author, who discovered the phylogenetic significance of cichlid otoliths, described *Eurotilapia*, a monotypic genus erected to accommodate the first otolith-based fossil cichlid. However, by the time of publication it was already known that these otoliths instead once belonged to a member of the Channidae (Gaemers, pers. comm.).

According to Casciotta & Arratia, a possible monophyly of the American Cichlidae is supported, albeit weakly, by two characters: 1) a strongly interdigitating suture between vomer and parasphenoid, and 2) the presence of a single lacrimal. But recent literature offers more to ponder. For instance, Irv Kornfield (1991: 104) mentions the difference in chromosome numbers between the New and the Old World Cichlids, while Sültmann *et al.* (1995: 1033) assign an "outgroup" position to the Neotropical cichlids in relation to their African counterparts. In consequence it becomes more and more difficult to believe that the family Cichlidae, as presently understood, is a monophyletic assemblage.

Nobody knows what the Cretaceous fishes that lived in the slowly widening southern Atlantic looked like. It is not hard to imagine that a marine ancestor of the Cichlidae entered the fresh waters of Africa, while a closely-related species entered the fresh waters of the New World. And this is not the only possible scenario.

Conclusions

Even before the theory of plate tectonics became generally accepted, the well-known vertebrate palaeontologist Alfred Sherwood Romer (1966: 69) warned against applying a strict vicariance model to the biogeography of the cichlid fishes. This warning was largely overlooked, or so it seems.

More recently Briggs (1995: 20) has stated that the cichlid fishes cannot be as old as many authors claim. But even this author persists in the view that the crossing of the southern Atlantic must have taken place during pre-Tertiary times. In the late Cretaceous this ocean was little more than a strait, and apparently Briggs feels that secondary freshwater fishes were at that time still capable of crossing that barrier. However, as we have seen earlier, it is most unlikely that the Cichlidae came into being before the great perciform radiation. And that, according to most palaeo-ichthyologists, took place during the late Eocene.

It is not impossible, however, that the southern part of the Atlantic Ocean was crossed by secondary freshwater fishes in Tertiary times. It has been demonstrated in many papers (see eg the contributions in Ciochon & Chiarelli, 1980), that rodents and primates also overcame that barrier during the Eocene. And if mammals could do so, then cichlids, being secondary freshwater fishes, may have as well. After all, Briggs (1995) also states that cichlids migrated from Africa to South America. Unfortunately he believes in a much earlier date.

It is thus only reasonable to conclude that Loiselle (*op. cit.*) is wrong in assuming that pterosaurs and ichthyosaurs included cichlid fishes in their diet; a cichlidophageous lifestyle was clearly not an option for these prehistoric animals.

References

BRIGGS, J.C. (1984) *Centres of origin in biogeography.* Biogeographical Monographs; 1, BSG, Leeds, UK.

BRIGGS, J.C. (1995) *Global biogeography.* Elsever Science, Netherlands.

CASCIOTTA, J. & G. ARRATIA (1993) Tertiary cichlid fishes from Argentina and reassessment of the phylogeny of New World cichlids. *Kaupia,* 2: 195-240.

COCHION, R.L. & A.B. CHIARELLI (eds) (1980) *Evolutionary biology of New World monkeys and continental drift.* Plenum Press.

GRAY, J. (1988) Evolution of the freshwater ecosystem; the fossil record. *Paleogeogr. Paleoclimatol. Paleoecol.,* 62: 1-114.

GREENWOOD, P.H. (1995) *Encyclopedia of fishes.* Weldon Owe, UK.

JOHNSON, G.D. (1993) Percomorph phylogeny; progress and problems. *Bull. Mar. Sci.,* 52 (1): 3-28.

KORNFIELD, I. (1991) Genetics; pp. 103-128; in: M. Keenleyside (ed.) *Cichlid fishes, behaviour, ecology and evolution.* Chapman & Hall, London.

KULLANDER, S. (1983) *A revision of the South American cichlid genus* Cichlasoma, Swedish Museum of Natural History, Stockholm, Sweden.

LOISELLE, P. (1995) The cichlids of Jurassic Park. *Cichlid News,* 4 (3): 18-23.

MAISEY, J. (1993) The enigmatic *Cichlasoma woodringi. TFH Mag.* 1993 (2): 160-161.

MICKLICH, N. & B. ROSCHER (1990) Neue Fischfunde aus der Baid-Formation (Oligozän, Tihamat Asir, SW Saudi-Arabien). *N. Jb. Geol. Paläont. Abh.* 180: 139-175.

MOORE, J.E.S. (1903) *The Tanganyika problem.* Hurst & Blackett, London.

PARENTI, L.R. (1981) A phylogenetic and biogeographic analysis of cyprinodontiform fishes (Teleostei: Atherinomorpha). *Bull. Amer. Mus. Nat. Hist.,* 168 (4): 335-557.

PATTERSON, C. (1993a) Teleostei. pp. 621-655; in: Benton, M. (ed) *The fossil record.* Chapman & Hall, London.

PATTERSON, C. (1993b) An overview of the early fossil record of Acanthomorphs. *Bull. Mar. Sci.* 52 (1): 29-59.

ROMER, A.S. (1966) *Vertebrate paleontology.* Third edition. University of Chicago Press.

SCHAEFFER, B. (1947) Cretaceous and Tertiary Actinopterygian fishes from Brazil. *Bull. Amer. Mus. Nat. Hist.,* 89: 1- 39.

SILVA SANTOS, R. da & H.R.S. SANTOS (1993) *Tremembichthys pauloensis* (Schaeffer, 1947) (Pisces; Cichlidae) da Formacao, Tremembé, Estado de São Paulo, Brasil. *An. Acad. bras. Ci.,* 65 (1): 41-55.

STAWIKOWSKI, R. (1993) *Retroculus* im Tapajos. *DATZ,* 46 (3): 144-145.

STIASSNY, M. (1981) The phyletic status of the family Cichlidae. *Neth. J. Zool.,* 31: 275-314.

STIASSNY, M. (1991) Phylogenetic intrarelationships of the family Cichlidae; an overview. pp. 1-35; in: M. Keenleyside (ed) Cichlid fishes; behaviour, ecology and evolution. Chapman & Hall.

STIASSNY, M. (1993) What is a cichlid? *TFH Mag.* 42 (3): 141-146.

STIASSNY, M. & N. RAMINOSOA (1994) The fishes of the inland waters of Madagascar. pp. 133-149; in: G. Teugels *et al.* (eds.) Biological diversity of African fresh- and brackish water fishes. *Ann. Kon. Mus. Mid. Afr.* 275.

SÜLTMANN, H., W. MAYER, F. FIGUEROA, H. TICHY & J. KLEIN (1995) Phylogenetic Analysis of Cichlid Fishes Using Nuclear DNA Markers, *Mol. Biol. Evol.* 12 (6): 1033 - 1047

WOODWARD, A.S. (1939) Tertiary fishes from Maranhão, Brasil. *Ann. Mag. nat. Hist. II,* 3: 450-453.

CICHLID ORGANISATIONS WORLDWIDE

Australia
Queensland Cichlid Group
P.O. Box 360
Wooloongabba, Queensland 4102

Victorian Cichlid Society
23 Mangana Drive
Mulgrave, Victoria 3170

Austria
Deutsche Cichliden Gesellschaft
Victor Kaplan Straße 1-9/1/3/12
A-1220 Wien

Belgium
Belgische Cichliden Vereninging
Kievitlaan 23
B-2228 Ranst

Denmark
Dansk Cichlide Selskab
Tølløsevej 76.
DK-2700 Brønshøj

France
Association France Cichlid
15 Rue des Hirondelles
F-67350 Dauendorf

Germany
Deutsche Cichliden Gesellschaft
Parkstraße 21a
D-33719 Bielefeld

Aquaristischer Arbeitskreis Leinetal
Interessegemeinschaft Cichliden
Ludwig-Prandtl-Straße 56
D-37077 Göttingen

Cichliden-Freunde Viernheim
Am Pfarrgarten 12
D-68519 Viernheim

Cichlidenklub Essen
Lohstraße 39
D-45359 Essen

VDA-Arbeitskreis Zwergcichliden
Richard-Holz-Straße 4
D-08060 Zwickau

Hungary
Sügérbarátok Klubja Budapest
Mészöly u. 6. II/3
H-1117 Budapest

Italy
Associazone Italiana Ciclidofili
Via Zucchini, 6
I-48018 Faenza

Japan
Japan Cichlid Association
Daizawa 4-46-3,Setagaya
Tokyo 155

Mexico
Grupo Mexicano de Ciclidófilos
Cordillera Karakorum 223B,
Lomas 3a sección
San Luis Potosí, S.L.P., 78216

Netherlands
Nederlandse Cichliden Vereniging
Boeier 31
NL-1625 CJ Hoorn

Cichlasoma
Teldersweg 86
NL-3911 PZ Rhenen

Slovakia
SZCH Klub Chovatelov Cichlíd
Príkopova 2
831 03 Bratislava

Sweden
Nordiska CiklidSällskapet
Plommonvägen 26
S-161 52 Bromma

Switzerland
Deutsche Cichliden Gesellschaft
Am Balsberg 1
CH-8302 Kloten

Taiwan (R.O.C.)
Taiwanese Cichlid Association
N°17, Lane 239, An-Ho Road
Taipei

United Kingdom
British Cichlid Association
248 Longridge, Knutsford
Cheshire, WA18 8PH

U. S. A.
American Cichlid Association
P.O. Box 5351
Naperville, IL 60567-5351

Adv. Cichl. Aquarists South California
P.O. Box 8173
San Marino, CA 91108

African Cichlid Club
3744 Forest Valley Court SE
Grand Rapids, MI 49508

Apistogramma Study Group
762 Hillside Avenue
Antioch, IL 60002

Atlantic Cichlid & Catfish Association
29 Pearsall Avenue
Jersey City, NJ 07305

Beach Cities Cichlid Association
2106 Manhattan Beach Boulevard/5
Redondo Beach, CA 90278

Cichlasoma Study Group
41W510 Rt. 20
Hampshire, IL 60140

Cichlid Hobbyists Eastern Wisconsin
3259 So. Swain Court
Milwaukee, WI 53207

Cichlid Seekers
2014 45th Street Court N.W.
Gig Harbor, Washington 98335

Fort Wayne Cichlid Association
9638 Manor Woods Rdf.
Ft. Wayne, IN 46804

Greater Chicago Cichlid Association
41W510 Rt. 20
Hampshire, IL 60140

Greater Cincinnati Cichlid Association
15 W. Southern Avenue
Covington, KY 41015

Illinois Cichlids and Scavengers
7807 Sunset Drive
Elmwood Park, IL 60635

Lake Erie Cichlid Association
1113 Sunset Road
Mayfield Heights, OH 44124

Michigan Cichlid Association
P.O. Box 59
New Baltimore, MI 48047

Milwaukee Cichlid Club
1926 Grange Avenue
Racine, WI 53403

Ohio Cichlid Association
7330 Ames Road
Parma, OH 44129

Oregon Cichlid Study Group
388 N. State Street
Lake Oswego, OR 97034

Pacific Coast Cichlid Association
P.O. Box 28145
San Jose, CA 95128

Pikes Peak Cichlid Association
P.O. Box 17176
Colorado Springs, CO 80935

Rift Valley Cichlids
15800 Laguna Avenue
Lake Elsinore, CA 92530

Rocky Mountain Cichlid Association
5065 W. Hinsdale Cir.
Littleton, CO 80123

Southern California Cichlid Association
P.O. Box 574
Midway City, CA 92655